Design and Techno
Key Stages 1 & 2

A practical guide to planning and implementation

Clare Benson

Longman

Acknowledgements

I would like to thank friends and former colleagues from Wolverhampton Local Education Authority and current colleagues in the Faculty of Education, Birmingham Polytechnic who have encouraged me to develop my interest in design and technology.

More particularly I would like to acknowledge the advice that I have received from Richard Ager, Anita Cliff, Chris Edwards, Sandra Fisher, Mary Hocking, Janet Le Carpentier, Graham Smith and members of Sandwell Science and Technology team.

Most of all my special thanks to John Benson for his helpful comments and encouragement throughout the writing of the book.

The children in the photograph on the front cover are from Woodthorne Infants School, Tettenhall, Wolverhampton.

Contents

Introduction

It seems only yesterday that the Design and Technology Working Group's Interim Report was first published and the catch phrase 'design and make a . . .' or even just 'make a . . .' began to assume such importance. In the following three years, many publications have emphasised the making of artefacts that move. Indeed, on visits to almost any primary school it was apparent that, if nothing else, children were fast becoming proficient at making buggies of every imaginable shape and size!

Gradually the nature of technology in the National Curriculum has emerged. It is clear now that it is not a subject with a precisely defined body of knowledge (although the programmes of study do outline the content that should be covered), but a subject that encompasses two broad capabilities: that of design and technology, and that of information technology – both of which cover and develop a wide range of curriculum areas and associated skills.

With the introduction of the core subjects, mathematics, English and science, many schools have decided to carry out 'mapping exercises' in an attempt to match their existing curriculum in these areas to those of the National Curriculum. They have then made changes to try to ensure that their children experience a broad and balanced curriculum that satisfies both school and National Curriculum requirements.

By contrast, few schools had – or have – an existing curriculum in any way matching the *Technology in the National Curriculum* document. Thus the implementation of this 'new' curriculum area will almost certainly involve schools in the creation of a policy document and appropriate schemes of work. It is true of course that in the past many of the cross-curricular activities in which children have been involved contained elements of design and technology capability. Unfortunately, however, it is not generally true that design and technology is 'something that we've been doing all along without calling it design and technology'. Some teachers have been doing it all along (at least in part), but many have not. In fact, it seems that whilst the most commonly covered element has been that involving making, the processes of identifying needs and evaluating have very often been omitted.

How then can changes be brought about to facilitate the intro-duction and development of design and technology in a school curriculum? It is not intended that this book should provide the approach, but rather that it should help to clarify the nature of technology in the National Curriculum and suggest various practical approaches to the planning and implementation of this 'new' area – an area which, at its best, really can do a great deal to enhance the whole of the primary curriculum.

This book includes a number of photocopiable sheets which will assist teachers in the planning, assessment and practical application of design and technology.

Part A
Technology in the National Curriculum Key Stages 1 and 2

Fig. 1.1 Technology in the National Curriculum

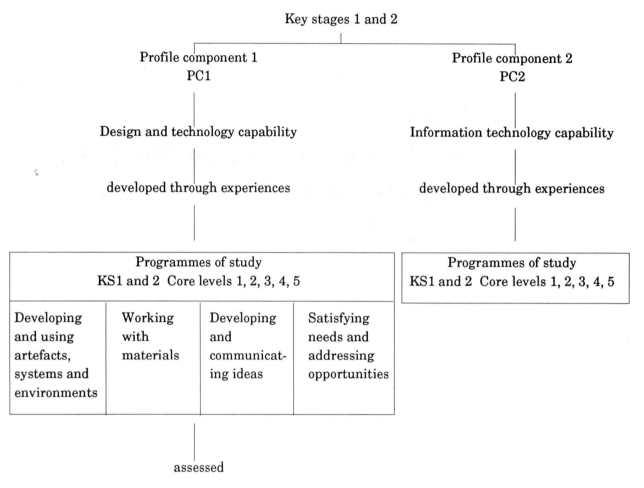

Key stages 1 and 2

Profile component 1 PC1	Profile component 2 PC2
Design and technology capability	Information technology capability
developed through experiences	developed through experiences

Programmes of study KS1 and 2 Core levels 1, 2, 3, 4, 5				Programmes of study KS1 and 2 Core levels 1, 2, 3, 4, 5
Developing and using artefacts, systems and environments	Working with materials	Developing and communicating ideas	Satisfying needs and addressing opportunities	

assessed

Attainment targets				Attainment target
AT1 Identifying needs and opportunities	AT2 Generating a design proposal	AT3 Planning and making	AT4 Evaluating	AT5 Information technology capability
KS1 Levels 1–3　　　KS2 Levels 2–5				KS1 Levels 1–3　　KS2 Levels 2–5

1
The document unravelled

It is not intended to offer here a detailed explanation of the meaning of the word 'technology' but to try to untangle some of the misconceptions, jargon and uncertainties surrounding the document *Technology in the National Curriculum* (DES, March 1990).

It is hardly surprising that there is confusion over this 'new' curriculum area, given the changing nature and title of the final document. Originally, technology was linked with two other major areas of the curriculum.

Links with science

Science and technology were linked in the first interim report of the two curriculum areas, and the subject 'science and technology' was introduced formally (in many instances for the first time) into the primary school curriculum. Science and Technology ESG (Educational Support Grant) teams were established and began to work in many primary schools throughout the country. Technology was then 'taken out' of the science document and became a foundation subject in its own right. Inevitably people made comments such as 'Why has the science been taken out of technology?' But science is still there, of course. Indeed, it has an important part to play in the programmes of study, with particular reference to mechanisms, energy, structures, forces and materials.

Links with craft, design and technology (CDT)

As with science, there has been confusion over the relationship between CDT and technology. It is now generally accepted that CDT plays an important part within technology, and indeed can be said to be subsumed within it. Moreover, many of the skills and underlying concepts are the same, but technology is now seen in a wider perspective.

Links with other areas

Home economics

Food and textiles are now seen as part of this wider perspective and children are to experience working with materials associated with these areas. Food should be seen as more than just cookery, involving aspects such as presentation, packaging and nutritional value; while textiles should be seen as more than just sewing, involving aspects such as dyeing, weaving and printing.

Art and design

Children may draw on skills and knowledge associated with this area of the curriculum particularly during the generating of a design proposal (for example sketching, drawing and using aesthetic judgments), and the planning and making of their solution (for example using a variety of graphic media).

Business studies

While this area is not usually identified as a separate subject in the primary school, it is now included within design and technology and links to the cross-curricular dimension – business and economic awareness.

Information technology (IT)

To many people, IT was synonymous with technology. In reality, as in all areas of the curriculum, design and technology activities should draw upon IT as and when appropriate.

English

The links are obvious, of course, with all aspects of English in the National Curriculum.

Cross-curricular links

All subjects and cross-curricular dimensions can be drawn upon during a variety of design and technology activities – the subject is truly cross-curricular in nature. Two examples are geography (of other cultures) and history (of other times).

What is included in the document *Technology in the National Curriculum*?

Technology can be said to be concerned with the identification of human needs and the ways in which those needs can be met by designing, making and evaluating existing and innovatory solutions. Indeed, the emphasis will almost certainly be on innovation rather than invention. These needs and opportunities are connected with, and arise from, the world in which we live.

Technology, as it appears in the National Curriculum document, is not a subject with an identified body of knowledge. It is composed of two profile components: design and technology capability and information technology capability (see Figure 1.1 on p. 6).

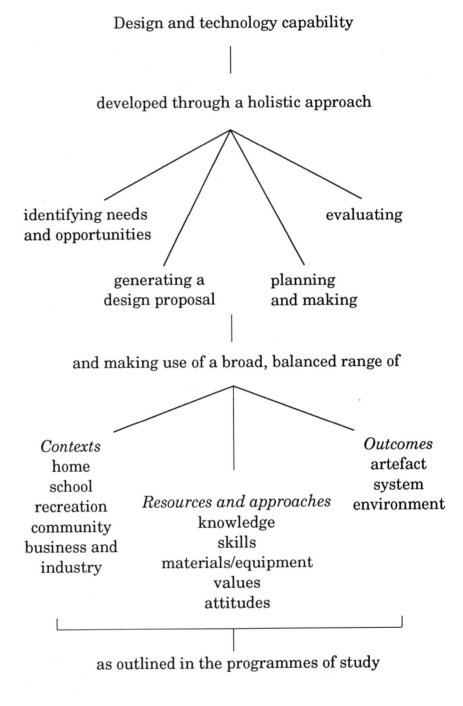

Design and technology capability

|

developed through a holistic approach

identifying needs
and opportunities   evaluating

generating a   planning
design proposal   and making

|

and making use of a broad, balanced range of

Contexts   *Outcomes*
home   artefact
school   system
recreation   *Resources and approaches*   environment
community   knowledge
business and   skills
industry   materials/equipment
                       values
                       attitudes

as outlined in the programmes of study

**Fig. 2.1 The application
of design and technology
capability**

2
Design and technology capability

What is meant by 'capability'?

The use of the word 'capability' indicates that the children will be developing an ability to identify needs, and to design, plan, make and evaluate new artefacts, systems and environments. In addition they will be able to evaluate existing products and offer suggestions for their modification. The application of this ability should be set within the overall context of the world in which they live (see Figure 2.1).

This capability is developed through a holistic process, involving all four processes in any one activity (see Figure 2.2). (The examples given alongside the programmes of study could be misleading in that they give the impression that each process can be assessed in isolation.)

This holistic process is neither linear nor cyclical but one in which the child moves backwards and forwards between the processes until the end of an activity (see Figure 2.3).

What is the meaning of these processes, each of which relates to an attainment target?

AT1 Identifying needs and opportunities

In the past, this part of the holistic process has often been pre-empted by the teacher. He/she has identified opportunities and needs, and has then presented them to his/her pupils, thus depriving them of an important opportunity to think for themselves. The task 'make a roundabout for the park' could be changed, however, to 'what could we make for the children to play on in the park? What movement could we incorporate? What mechanisms could we use?' Although greater teacher input may be needed throughout Key Stage 1, pupils should be encouraged to identify needs and opportunities for themselves and to state them clearly. Devising and using questionnaires as part of a survey to help identify a particular need is just one method the children may use to gather any necessary information during this process.

**Fig. 2.2 The development
of design and technology
capability**

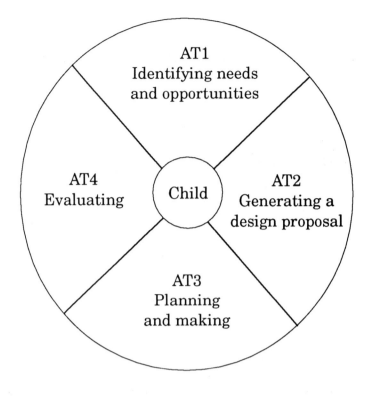

**Fig. 2.3 Moving through
the holistic process**

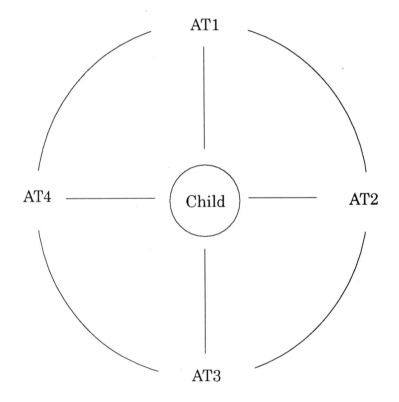

AT2 Generating a design

This will involve the children in considering a number of solutions
for the need that they have identified. Constraints such as time, cost
and the availability and properties of materials should be considered, while an important role could be played at this stage by:

- brainstormings
- sketches
- models
- plans
- drawings

- discussions
- flowcharts
- recipes
- patterns
- testing

AT3 Planning and making

This will involve the children in working towards achieving their design proposal. This would include choosing their own resources, including materials and equipment, in order that they can make one or more of the following outcomes: artefact, system and/or environment.

AT4 Evaluating

This will involve the children in evaluating both their finished product and the processes in which they have been involved:

- at different stages during the project;
- at the end of their project.

In addition they will be involved in the evaluation of:

- products of other times, (links with history and geography);
- products of other cultures (multicultural dimension).

What then is the relationship between these four processes and the programmes of study?

The programmes of study for design and technology capability, as set out in the National Curriculum, outline the content that is to be covered in the classroom, through which the processes can be developed.

Four main strands have been identified:

Developing and using artefacts, systems and environments

This relates to an ability to:

- develop and use systems;
- work with and use a variety of structures, mechanisms, forces and energy sources.

Working with materials

This relates to an ability to:

- use and join a range of materials;
- act safely;
- avoid wastage of materials.

Developing and communicating ideas
This relates to an ability to use various appropriate methods to share and communicate ideas.

Satisfying needs and addressing opportunities
This relates to an ability to:

- ascertain the likes/dislikes of others, taking into account, for example, differing backgrounds;
- evaluate own products and those of others;
- take into account economic considerations.

Activities which enable children to develop their capability through these four strands should be set in different contexts, for example:

- home
- school
- recreation
- community
- business and industry

Although the list is not set out in any order of priority, it is often said that children should start from the familiar, only moving later to the unfamiliar. Home and school will therefore be very relevant contexts for young children, while business and industry will almost certainly play a more important role at Key Stage 2. Children do not have to experience each context in each key stage, but of course it is important to provide balanced experiences.

The activities should allow for a variety of outcomes (see Figure 2.4). All design and technology activities must have one or more of these outcomes.

Fig. 2.4 Outcomes of design and technology activities

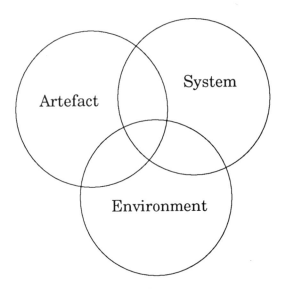

Artefact
This is an object made by the children. Examples might include a cushion, a book, a game, a toy, a cake, a picture.

Environment
This is a surrounding created or developed by the children. Examples might include a shop, a clinic, a garden centre, a herb garden, a home corner.

System
This is a set of objects or activities which perform a task. Examples could include a party, a puppet show, a fire drill, traffic lights, an alarm system and the putting out of PE equipment.

The overlapping circles highlight the inter-relationship between the three outcomes. While there may be a main outcome from an activity, it is possible that other outcomes will also result.

For example, suppose the activity was to organise a leaver's party, based on a desert island theme. The main outcome could be *system* (the whole party). However, there might also be *artefacts* (e.g. invitations, cakes, decorations) and an *environment* (desert island surroundings) as part of the main outcome.

Implicit in the four strands are the *knowledge* and *skills* that will be experienced and developed during a variety of design and technology activities.

Knowledge
'We are dealing with an activity which goes across the curriculum, drawing on and linking with a wide range of subjects' *(Design and Technology for Ages 5–16* 1.8 DES, June 1989).

At Key Stages 1 and 2, science, mathematics, art and design, information technology and English are key areas, but all the foundation subjects and cross-curricular dimensions will feed into the body of knowledge upon which children will draw.

Skills
NCC has identified:

Common skills
that are common to many design and technology activities and will be applied very often. Examples include:

RESEARCHING	RECORDING AND COMMUNICATING
communicating	drawing
classifying	observing
evaluating	selecting information
interpreting	writing
predicting	reporting

PLANNING	GROUP SKILLS
analysing	listening
co-ordinating	talking
managing	negotiating
scheduling	questioning
brainstorming	co-operating
	respecting others

Fundamental skills
that are fundamental to children's design and technology work but are specific to certain materials. Thus they may be developed through specially devised tasks, allowing the children to draw on these skills at a later date. Examples include:

MAKING	NUMERICAL SKILLS	DESIGNING
cutting	predicting	sketching
joining	estimating	drawing
mixing	measuring	constructing models
finishing	costing	pattern making
weaving	tallying	recipe making
dyeing		
baking		

Materials and equipment

Children should be given the opportunity to work with a range of materials, including:

- textiles;
- graphic materials (such as paint, paper, photographs);
- construction materials (such as clay, wood, construction kits);
- food.

There is no specific equipment itemised in the document but suitable items are suggested in chapter six.

Values

While children working within Key Stage 1 can begin to make value judgments, greater emphasis may be placed on the development of these judgments within Key Stage 2.

Economic
The product may look good but is it economic to produce?

Aesthetic
The product may be economical to produce but is it attractive enough for people to want to buy it?

Environmental

The product may smell nice and look good but is it 'environmentally friendly'?

Technological

The product may use the latest electronic development but is it really the most suitable product for the job?

Social

The product may benefit the individual but does it benefit the needs of the community as a whole?

Attitudes

The document does not identify specific attitudes to be encouraged, but incorporates them within the programmes of study and the statements of attainment. Certainly, the following attitudes should be developed not only through design and technology but through many other areas of the curriculum as well.

Open-mindedness

This may be developed through the generation of a design proposal in which different solutions, involving flexibility of thinking, may be needed.

Perseverance

This may be developed through the making and modifying stages of the entire process.

Co-operation

This may be developed through the entire activity and may include sensitivity and tolerance of other's ideas, beliefs and racial identity.

Reliability

This may be developed at any stage of an activity which involves working with others. For example, it is important that others can rely on a part for the product being completed on time.

Self-discipline

This may be developed through, for example, the safe use of a variety of tools and the organisation of materials and equipment.

Self-confidence

This may be developed in particular through involvement in discussions, presentations and evaluations.

3
Information technology capability and its role within design and technology

Information technology is concerned with the collection, storage, processing and presentation of information by electronic means.

To many people IT means solely the use of computers, but it is broader than that. In fact, electronic devices are found in many everyday objects, from telephones, videos and tape recorders to programmable toys. The emphasis on the use of computers may be related to two main factors:

1. There is no extra money being made available to schools to build up resources such as tape recorders, camcorders or even telephones. There has been some funding for computers, indicating, rightly or wrongly, that these should be the priority.
2. The use of computers has caused concern to teachers who were unfamiliar with their use and application.

Information technology capability

Although IT capability is included within the Technology document, it should be remembered that IT permeates the whole curriculum. The non-statutory guidelines identify five strands which together will enable children to develop their IT capability:

- communicating information
- handling information
- modelling
- measurement and control
- applications and effects of IT

How can IT capability be developed through design and technology activities? The following examples illustrate some of the opportunities that design and technology activities afford for the development of IT.

Communicating information
Experience of word processing programs may be gained through creating:

letters to ask   labels
for information   notices
leaflets   questionnaires
posters   reports
newspapers

Experience of graphics programs may be gained by the production of:

invitations   cards
plans   posters
pictures for a book   wrapping paper designs
wallpapers   fabric designs (e.g. for
                            clothing)

Experience of a simple desk top publishing (DTP) program may be gained through the production of:

newspapers   leaflets
broadsheets   magazines
newsletters

The production of photographs and video and audio tape provides further experience and understanding of how information can be communicated.

Handling information

Experience of the use of databases and spreadsheets may be gained through the collection of:

- information from surveys, e.g. which flavour do you prefer? which fabric do you prefer? which new service would be of most use?
- information from investigations, e.g. which is the strongest fabric, which are the smoothest-running wheels?
- information to help with running a school fund-raising event or costing a project such as a garden area for the school.

Experience may be gained in using a tape recorder for storing information.

Modelling

Although the main focus for developing this area lies outside Key Stages 1 and 2, early experiences can be built upon at a later stage. Modelling can be used to simulate the real world, when working in a real life situation is impractical. For example, by using a program such as Locks, children can discover what would happen to the amount of water in the locks if rainfall decreased over a set period of time.

Spreadsheets can be used to model a budget for the production of an item such as a magazine. For example, it would be possible to see how production costs might increase/decrease depending on the number produced.

Modelling can also be used for fantasy situations and adventure programs may provide a starting point from which children can develop their own games. By exploring the game, they gain an understanding of its design, which they may use in the construction of their own board games.

Measurement and control
Experience may be gained through the use of:

- a tape recorder to record an interview or piece of music for a play;
- a cooker;
- Big Track, Roamer, Valiant Turtle or Pip;
- control models to switch something on and off, open and shut, move up and down;
- a sewing machine;
- a kiln.

Applications and effects of IT
Experience of this strand may be gained through researching and evaluating the use of IT in everyday situations. The following questions may prove useful in developing capability in this area.

- What uses of IT can be identified:
  - in school?
  - in the home?
  - in the shops/local community?
  - in other places that the children visit?
- How could this information be recorded?
- How does IT make life easier?
- Is IT always:
  - quicker
  - easier
  - cheaper
  - more accurate
    than other means of storing and retrieving information?
- What are the drawbacks of using IT? – (Many teachers have experienced feelings of frustration, anger and despair when a program will not load/save or a taped radio recording mysteri-ously erases itself.)

Part B
Planning and implementation: a whole-school approach

4
A curriculum audit

With the introduction of the National Curriculum there has been a general change in attitude towards the planning and implementation of the curriculum in the primary school. In particular the idea of a whole-school approach is being adopted for the first time in many schools and planning is following a curriculum model similar to the one outlined in Figure 4.1.

Fig. 4.1 Model for curriculum audit

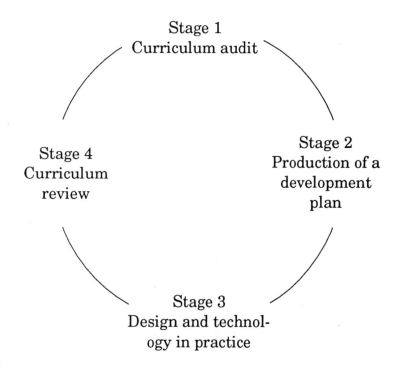

Stage 1
Curriculum audit

Stage 2
Production of a
development
plan

Stage 3
Design and technol-
ogy in practice

Stage 4
Curriculum
review

The following section has been planned in such a way that it is possible to link into it at the stage that is most appropriate for the individual school. However, as the planning process is continuous, it is envisaged that schools will move through all four stages, although not necessarily starting at Stage 1. It is also quite possible for individual teachers to use the model, making their own modifications as appropriate.

The information that is gathered can be used to identify and prioritise any action that is needed. It can be collated under four main headings:

- Content;
- Organisation and management;
- Resources;
- Assessment and record keeping.

To facilitate this audit, the curriculum audit record sheets on pages 28 and 29 could be photocopied and given to the most appropriate person or persons for completion.

Content

Before any review can take place, it is important that staff are able to identify design and technology within the curriculum.

- What do the staff understand by design and technology capability, information technology capability, and technology in the National Curriculum?
- What links between them do they perceive?
- Are there existing schemes of work for design and technology?
- What design and technology activities have been carried out in the last year?
- How do these activities contribute to the requirements of the National Curriculum in terms of programmes of study and attainment targets?
- Have all the attainment targets been visited in the activities? (There is a need to ensure that AT1 is part of the holistic process that children must work through in any design and technology activity.)
- Within a planning stage, such as a key stage, has a balance been struck between longer and shorter activities, closed and open tasks, types of outcomes, and the contexts and materials that have been used?
- Have the children been involved in some separate skill-based tasks to enable them to develop new skills that they can then use in design and technology activities?
- What strategies have been identified to ensure progression?
- What strategies have been employed to ensure that an equal opportunities policy is carried out? (While there is no dispute as to the importance of such a policy in all areas of the curriculum, it is particularly important that it is addressed within design and technology which, by its very nature, can give rise to unwanted stereotyping by children, parents and teachers alike.)

Organisation and management

Having identified some of the main issues surrounding the content of design and technology, consideration needs to be given to organisation.

- Is there an existing school policy?
- How is design and technology incorporated into the curriculum? Possibilities include through topic work, as a subject area in its own right, through planned happenings, through spontaneous happenings or through a mixture of these;
- What planning takes place to ensure that the children experience a broad and balanced curriculum?
- What strategies are employed to enable staff and pupils to share the ideas and findings resulting from the activities that the children have undertaken?
  Possibilities include assemblies, displays, presentations, newsletters, staff meetings, and liaison with feeder schools.
- What strategies are employed to inform staff of information concerning current curriculum developments, INSET provision and resources?
- What strategies are employed to help parents and governors gain an understanding of, and information about, this 'new' area of the curriculum? Possibilities include regular newsletters, provision of short workshops both in and outside school hours, simple activity sheets to be used at home and encouragement to work alongside the children in the classroom.
- What teaching strategies are used to deliver design and technology? Possibilities include class teaching, group work, pair work, individual work or a mixture.
- What criteria are used to determine the composition of the groups? Possibilities include friendship, ability, mixed ability, interest.
- What role does the co-ordinator play in all of this?
  Is there an identified person with responsibility either solely for design and technology or jointly for this and other curriculum areas?
- What links are made with co-ordinators for other curriculum areas, especially those of art, IT, and science? Links might include curriculum policies and planning, resources, record keeping and assessment.
- What plans are there for an INSET programme for the staff?
- How will staff identify their priorities in terms of INSET provision?

Resources

An audit could prove an ideal opportunity for all cupboards and corners to be searched so that a complete list of resources can be made. Resources which traditionally may not be associated with design and technology should not be overlooked.

Resources will include:

- equipment
- materials
- tools (including those used for cookery, art and textiles)
- computer programs
- construction kits
- books for pupil use
- books for staff use

The data could be recorded on to a record sheet (see pp. xx and xx) and, if time allows, put on to a database. As well as providing an instant record of the current availability of equipment, the database will facilitate the review and updating of equipment in the future.

- What method(s) of storage are there in the school?
- What is kept in individual classrooms?
- What is kept in a central store?
- Who is responsible for keeping the resources tidy, and for identifying and replenishing consumable stock?
- Is someone responsible for informing staff about new resources that are available? How is this new information to be gathered?
- What links are there between the school and possible sources of resources (local industry, museum, art gallery)?
- What strategies are used to ensure the best possible deployment of both teaching staff and other adult helpers?
  Possibilities include teaching with others, teaching to a strength, provision of additional adult support during practical sessions and utilising parent helpers to organise/make resources.

Assessment and record-keeping

There will inevitably be links between design and technology and other curricular areas and it may be that schools have already decided to assess skills across the curriculum. However, there are certain particular features that will need to be addressed in connection with this curriculum area. Because statements of attainment relate only to the process and not to the detailed content, it is important to record information such as the contexts, outcomes, materials and mechanisms used in each activity.

- Is there an overall school policy for assessment and record-keeping? If so, will it be suitable for design and technology?
- What information relating to the children's work is kept? How is it/will it be selected?
- Where will the evidence be kept? (Models present particular problems.)
- What strategies are used to ensure that the holistic process of design and technology (that is, all four ATs in one activity) is being assessed?

A generalised overview of assessment and recording may be sufficient at this time. After children and staff have taken part in further activities, the staff will have more concrete experiences on which to develop ideas. (This is an issue which is tackled in more depth in chapter 7 (p.58).

Curriculum audit record sheet 1

Resources: materials, equipment, tools, computer programs, books	Item	Where stored

Curriculum audit record sheet 2

Construction kit	Where stored	Age range suitability	Evaluation to include: size of pieces, type of joints, motorised types of models that can be made, gender neutral, teachers/pupils' manual, number of children that could use kit at one time

5
The INSET day: focus for the development plan

The audit will not necessarily solve problems, indeed it will probably serve to identify more than was originally envisaged. Nonetheless it will provide information from which a development plan can be initiated.

The initial focus could be provided by holding an INSET day (or days) to enable the entire staff to be part of, and to contribute to, the plan. The chosen programme will obviously depend on the ideas and experiences of the staff.

INSET day 1 Awareness-raising day
INSET day 2 Towards a whole-school policy.

Whatever the programme for the day, there are some general matters that always need to be considered. Most points are obvious but a checklist can help to maximise the success of the day.

- Decide who is to have overall responsibility for the day. If one person takes this job on, there is less likelihood of the duplication of jobs or, worse, of jobs not being done at all.
- Try to involve all the staff in the planning of the day.
- Ensure that external speakers are informed well in advance when and where the INSET is to take place and that all their requirements are noted and met.
- Check that domestic arrangements such as heating, food, drinks and timings are confirmed.
- Check that all the materials that will be needed are readily accessible.
- Distribute a timetable for the day.
- Try to create a balance between listening, discussion, and practical activity.

To gain the most from the day, coffee breaks can be set during practical tasks or can be combined with the opportunity for staff to examine items such as equipment and books.

INSET day 1: Awareness-raising day

Morning session

What is technology?
Ask staff to work in pairs. What words do they associate with technology? Feed back and discuss the nature of technology in the National Curriculum, design and technology capability and IT capability.

Identification of the design and technological process
(Information in Part A, on pages 7–20 could be used.)

Short practical activity to give staff a common experience
Suggestions include: make a hat, a badge, a finger puppet, a container for dolly mixtures or sugar, an open sandwich, a card, a poster or a piece of jewellery.

From 'making' to design and technology
All these are 'making' activities. How could they be changed into design and technology activities? What context, what outcome, what needs and opportunities could be identified? What evaluations could be made?

Which broad areas have been covered?
Check against programmes of study.

Which broad areas could be assessed through such an activity?
Check against the levels of attainment. What could be assessed in other curriculum areas?

Afternoon session

Planning a design and technology activity
The activity could be chosen from those suggested in the Activity planning and development sheets (pp.77–114).

Planning and making one outcome of the above activity
The outcome may be an artefact, system or environment. This activity could lead to the development of teachers' own practical skills and techniques perhaps through modelling with junk or construction kits. Ideas could be taken from the Practical skills and techniques sheets (pp.115–131).

Display of books, equipment and materials available in school
Allow time for examination and discussion of these.

INSET day 2: Towards a whole-school policy

Morning session

Staff could meet in groups and work through the following stages:

- Identify all the design and technology activities that their children have undertaken in the last year.
- How did the activities arise? Was it through topic work, specific design and technology projects, or a spontaneous event?
- Map these activities against the programmes of study. What gaps are there?
- What kinds of activities would now be needed to enable the children to experience a balanced coverage of the programmes of study?
- How can design and technology best be fitted into the whole school curriculum?
- What specific skills may have to be taught to the children for use in design and technology activities?
- What resources have been used? What essential items must be obtained in the very near future?

Afternoon session

1. Planning for the following term's design and technology activities using the information gained from the morning session.
2. Development of teachers' own practical skills through a task based on the previous activity.

6
The planning begins

Content

Having identified the school position regarding design and technology and raised an awareness of some of the major issues surrounding its implementation, whole-school planning for design and technology can begin.

When writing the schemes of work, it should be remembered that the content in the design and technology document is found in the programmes of study, not in the attainment targets; and that this sets it apart from the core curricular areas. Design and technology does not have a precisely defined body of knowledge to be covered or programmes of study and attainment targets that relate directly to one other.

What is a scheme of work?

It is a description of the work that will be undertaken with the children over a set period of time, e.g. a key stage. It outlines the knowledge, skills and concepts that will be covered and the methods by which they will be introduced. Each scheme should be set in the context of previous and future schemes.

Writing a scheme of work

The programmes of study provide the minimum content that must be covered at each key stage. Two main methods of incorporating them into a scheme of work are possible.

1. The programmes of study can be grouped in different ways to create activities. This will ensure that all the programmes will be covered at least once.

   But – it may lead to contrived activities in order to cover certain aspects of the programmes.

2. The design and technology activities can provide the starting points and then the children's experiences can be matched against the programmes of study. This allows the activities to be set in the context of the on-going work of the class.

   But – it may lead to gaps in the content that has to be covered. It is probable that most schools will favour the latter method because it allows them to retain any existing rotation of topics/

themes that have been planned since the introduction of the National Curriculum. Provided the chosen topics are broad, it should be possible to create a range of opportunities to ensure the programmes of study are covered.

To enable teachers to map activities against the programmes of study, planning sheets can be used. Two examples are offered. Planning sheets 1a and 1b (pp.43–48) set out the programmes of study so that the core and the levels of each part of the programme are combined.

Planning sheets 2a and 2b (pp.50–53) divide the statements in the programmes of study into three:

- those that relate to almost any activity;
- those that relate to many activities;
- those that relate to a few activities.

Dividing the statements up in this way will make it easier to identify both specialised and generalised statements. Different coloured markers could be used to indicate the coverage experienced through different activities.

While these planning sheets can be used as a general record of the work that has been covered by a topic, records for individual pupils will still be required, of course.

When a general outline of the scheme of work has been completed, it might be appropriate to consider the following issues:

- The teaching strategies that are to be used. Possibilities include class lessons, individual, pair and group work.
- The criteria that will be used to determine the groups. These may include groups that are based on friendship, ability, mixed ability or gender.
- The main skills that will be developed. The emphasis on different skills may vary with the child's developing capability at different key stages.
- The ways in which these skills will be developed:
  - through design and technology activities;
  - through short tasks that focus on a particular skill (often connected with making) which can then be incorporated into a design and technology activity at a later date.
- The need to ensure a balance in the contexts and outcomes.
- The most appropriate resources that will be required.
- The ways in which the issue of progression is being addressed.

Progression

While it is anticipated that schemes of work will show progression, it is left to staffs and/or individual teachers to identify detailed progression.

General guidance can be found in the programmes of study but a major concern is that the identified progression should be based on a secure foundation.

1. Moving from Key Stage 1 to Key Stage 2, the children should increasingly experience activities which encourage economic awareness and initiative as well as the evaluation of products of others.
2. Studying the terminology, the following progression can be identified:

    use ⟶ choose

    use ⟶ understand a purpose for

    use ⟶ create
3. Included in the non-statutory guidance, the following strands have been identified:
    *   an increase in knowledge, skills, and understanding;
    *   moving from familiar to unfamiliar contexts;
    *   meeting needs which demand more complex or difficult solutions;
    *   pupils' awareness of their growing design and technology capability.

A more detailed analysis of aspects of progression is outlined in Progression sheets 1, 2 and 3 (pp.54–56). Schools could use these sheets as a basis from which to devise their own.

Progression in IT will also need to be considered, not only in the software that the children use but also in the general capability of the children, as outlined in the five IT strands in the non-statutory guidance.

NCC identify these areas in which progression can be shown as:

*   carrying out more complex tasks;
*   moving from a familiar problem to an unfamiliar one;
*   applying more advanced skills;
*   becoming more independent and confident in using IT;
*   using more sophisticated software.

To help schools plan for a progression in the use of software, a whole-school approach to its use could be discussed and mapped as in the Software progression sheet (p.57) based on the NCC model.

Organisation and management

The main concern will be with the production of a school policy for design and technology and the role that the co-ordinator will play in its overall management.

School policy for design and technology

General points

The policy will cover the purposes, nature and management of design and technology in the school.

While the headteacher and the co-ordinator may play a major role in organising and collating information, it is important that the policy evolves through discussion and debate with the whole staff. In addition, it could be useful to consult with representatives from local industry, LEA and professional bodies.

It is important that the policy is seen as a working document, that it is constantly updated, and that it is useful to members of staff, the headteacher, parents and governors.

The following is offered as a framework but each school will make its own modifications to meet its own particular needs. Matters that could be included are:

- a statement relating to the nature of design and technology capability, its relationship with other curriculum areas, and the reasons for the decision to include or exclude information technology capability;
- the methods of including design and technology within the curriculum (through topics, as a separate subject);
- an indication of the approaches to be used to ensure that the following issues are addressed:
  • equal opportunities,
  • progression,
  • continuity (between classes, schools);
- the availability and organisation of resources;
- the assessment of pupils;
- the methods of record-keeping to be employed to indicate:
  • the work that has been covered,
  • the children's individual achievements;
- an indication of the provision for staff INSET needs.

The role of the co-ordinator

With the pressure on staff to 'take on' an area of the curriculum, it may well be that the person who has design and technology as his/her area of responsibility does not feel an 'expert' in the field and/or already has another area to oversee such as science or IT. If the former is the case, this should not be cause for concern as the role is one relating mainly to organisation and management and requires such qualities as enthusiasm, commitment and a willingness to work co-operatively. If the latter is the case, it will be important for the staff, governors and parents to understand the links between those other subjects and design and technology so that they realise design and technology is a curriculum area in its own right. It is often the case, for instance, that people believe that design and technology is 'just the appliance of science'.

The following guidelines are offered for those taking on the role of co-ordinator.

Co-ordination
The role is not one of 'doing it all'. Co-ordination means the bringing together of ideas, materials and people. This collaborative effort should include all those involved (see Figure 6.1).

Fig. 6.1
Co-ordinating people

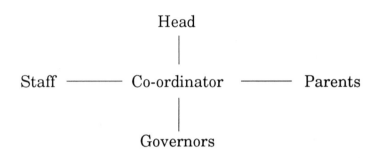

Information
It is important that the co-ordinator keeps information up-to-date and disseminates, it to all those involved (see Figures 6.2 and 6.3).

Fig. 6.2
Acquiring information

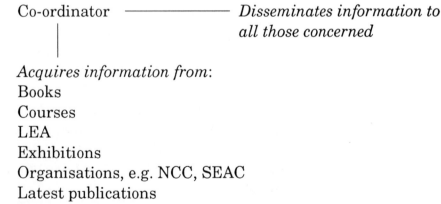

Planning and implementation
The co-ordinator should be able to offer advice and support at different levels.

Resources
An effort should be made to maintain equipment in good working order, and materials should be kept tidy, labelled and complete. A checklist of present stock and its whereabouts may prove useful.

It will be helpful to update staff and pupil reference books and to be able to meet staff requests for source books offering ideas on specific subjects.

Fig. 6.3
Disseminating
information

Co-ordinator ———— *Disseminates information through:*

Staff meetings
Parents' evenings
Governors' meetings
Parents' workshops
Information leaflets
Activity sheets for parents and
    children

Fig. 6.4
Ways of providing
advice and support

Co-ordinator ———— *Provides advice and support on*
planning and implementation by:

Working alongside colleagues
Organising INSET
Overseeing issues of continuity and
    progression
Offering ideas and sources for new
    ideas

Resources

No amount of planning and organisation can effect the implementation of design and technology without an adequate and well organised supply of resources. Because some of the tools and equipment are used by both adults and children, it is difficult to make separate lists for Key Stages 1 and 2. Schools should decide for themselves what they feel is most suitable for their children, and they will obviously bear in mind such matters as progression, familiarity and safety. (Thus, while such tools as glue guns and craft knives can be very useful, it would be ill-advised to allow Key Stage 1 children to use them.)

The following suggestions for materials and equipment are offered as a check list which schools can use to help them devise their own 'shopping lists'. The suggested items have been divided into four groups:

• items that may be used frequently;
• items that may be used less frequently;
• construction kits;
• computer programs.

Items used frequently.
These should be stored somewhere that is easily accessible to both adults and children.

Materials

different types of paper	card
Plasticine	variety of fabrics
cotton wool	elastic

junk materials, including boxes, plastic containers, cylindrical rolls.

Equipment

FIXINGS TO INCLUDE:

glue gun and glue sticks	Sellotape
masking tape	Pritt Stick
white PVA glue	brass paper fasteners
paper-clips	drawing pins
mapping pins	stapler and staples
wool	string
wire	pipe-cleaners
rubber bands	large sewing needles

CUTTING EQUIPMENT TO INCLUDE:

scissors (left and right handed)	snips (adult use)
craft knives and cutting board	
hole puncher	

ART EQUIPMENT TO INCLUDE:

pencils (ordinary and coloured)	wax crayons
felt pens	variety of paints
variety of brushes	mixing palettes
chalk	charcoal
pastels	inks

Items used less frequently
These could be stored in a more central place to enable all staff to gain easy access to them.

Materials

Corriflute	plastic
variety of fabrics	clay
variety of threads	dyes
wool	string
art straws	plaster of Paris
Modroc	balloons
polystyrene (NB	syringes
Safe cutting)	matchsticks
tubing	candles
lolly sticks	

variety of wood such as balsa, different diameters of dowelling, square section wood, off cuts;

variety of non-perishable foodstuffs such as flour, sugar;

junk, including boxes, containers, egg boxes, cylindrical tubes.

Equipment

fabric crayons	video (rented or borrowed)
Velcro	washing-up bowl
variety of fastenings	fabric pins
variety of screws and nails	pattern paper
saucepans – metal and clear glass	mixing bowls
scales	grater
measuring jug	wok
cooling tray	colander
	camera

variety of baking containers, including tins for bread, buns, cakes;

electrical equipment to include batteries, bulbs and holders, wire, crocodile clips, motors, buzzers and switches.

TOOLS TO INCLUDE:

junior hacksaw	bench hook
bradawl	G-clamp
hand drill	jig
vice	steel rule
different sized screwdrivers	wire strippers
hammer	clay tools
knitting needles	scraperboard/tools
sewing machine	variety of needles
pinking shears	home-made looms

cookery utensils, including whisk, beater, knives, forks, spoons, spatula, can opener, scoop, rolling pin, dough cutters;

cooker (can be rented very cheaply – contact your local Electricity showroom).

Construction kits

The suggested kits have been divided into two groups, according to their suitability for Key Stages 1 and 2. However, teachers should decide what is most appropriate according to their own children's experiences and manipulative skills. The following are probably most suited to Key Stage 1:

Bauplay	Construx
Duplo	Georello
Lego box 1053	Lasy (Jumbo, Midi)
Mobilo	Play and Build
Polydron	Quadro
Reoclick	Sticklebricks
Briomec	

The following could also be considered suitable for Key Stage 2:

Capsela	Teko
Fischer Technik	Technic Lego
Lasy, Reoclick (both have motorised parts)	

While it is difficult to deny the value of construction kits, it is equally important for children to develop their understanding of ideas about mechanisms and structures, for example, through modelling with junk materials.

Computer programs

The following programs are a cross-section of those that could be used by the children during their design and technology activities. The children will use these as and when it is appropriate.

Communicating information

WORD PROCESSING PROGRAMS

Minnie (Nimbus)
Write (Nimbus, 480Z)
Writeon (Nimbus)

DESK TOP PUBLISHING

Caxton (Nimbus, 480Z)
NewSPAper (Nimbus, 480Z)
Front page extra (Nimbus, 480Z, BBC)

GRAPHICS

Paintpot (Nimbus)
Paintspa (Nimbus)
PC Paint (Nimbus)

Brush (Nimbus)
Polanski (Nimbus)

Handling information

Branch (Nimbus, 480Z, BBC)

Grasshopper (Nimbus)

Ourfacts (Nimbus, 480Z, BBC)

Questionnaire (Nimbus)

Grass (Nimbus, 480Z, BBC)
Modelling
Granny's Garden
Dragon's World
Suburban Fox (Nimbus)

Lost Frog
Annabel's Raven

Measurement and control

Logo (Arrow 480Z, Dart BBC)
Control logo (480Z, BBC)

The local IT centre/advisory teacher could be approached for more specific help.

The organisation of the resources

Where to store
This will obviously depend on the amount of available space but it might be that each class has a basic kit, while larger, more expensive or less frequently used items are kept in a central store.

How to store
Drawer units, curver boxes, strong cardboard boxes, stacking trays, plastic dustbins, carry-all holders with handles, tool boards and mobile storage units are all suitable. Whichever is used, the system should be labelled clearly and stacked carefully.

Before tool boards are moved, the tools on them should be secured.

Thought should be given to the security aspect of an open-access policy to resources.

Who is to supervise?
Initially, it may be the person with responsibility for resources or for design and technology. It would be useful to develop a system that is known to all pupils and staff to ensure that:

- the whereabouts of all equipment is known to everyone;
- all equipment is put tidily away in the correct place;
- any items that are required are listed and given to the co-ordinator.

Planning sheet 1a

Design and technology capability	Programmes of study Key Stage 1
Developing and using artefacts, systems and environments **Core** • know that a system is made of related parts which are combined for a purpose; • identify the jobs done by parts of a system; • give a sequence of instructions to produce a desired result; • recognise and make models of simple structures around them; • use sources of energy to make things move; • identify what should be done and ways in which work should be organised; **Level 1** • recognise that materials can be linked in various ways to make or allow movement; • make simple objects for a purpose; **Level 2** • recognise that control involves making things work as desired; **Level 3** • recognise pattern in the structure of objects; • know that objects are changed by the forces applied to them; • know that systems have inputs, processes and outputs and recognise these in a variety of simple systems: • use simple mechanisms to transfer motion; • recognise that a source of energy is required to make things work; • organise their work, taking account of constraints; • realise that, when working in teams, people may have specialist roles; • use a variety of energy devices. **Working with materials** **Core** • explore and use a variety of materials to design and make things; • recognise that materials are processed in order to change or control their properties; • recognise that many materials are available and have different characteristics which make them appropriate for different tasks; • join materials and components in simple ways; • use materials and equipment safely; No extension level 1 **Level 2** • choose materials and equipment to make objects; • investigate the properties of materials in the course of their designing and making; • identify natural and manufactured materials; • use simple hand tools, and know how to look after them; • care for their surroundings; **Level 3** • recognise that materials and equipment need to be safely stored and maintained; • be aware of the dangers of the misuse of materials and equipment, and the consequent risk of accidents; • use alternative means of joining materials; • recognise the appropriate tools for working with a variety of materials.	**Activity**

**Planning sheet 1a
continued**

Design and technology capability	Programmes of study Key Stage 1
	Activity

Developing and communicating ideas

Core
- use imagination, and their own experiences, to generate and explore ideas;
- represent and develop ideas by drawing, models, talking, writing, working with materials;
- find out, sort, store and present information for use in designing and making;

No extension levels 1 & 2

Level 3
- develop a range of simple skills used in drawing and modelling.

Satisfying needs and addressing opportunities

Core
- know that goods are bought, sold and advertised;
- realise that resources are limited, and choices must be made;
- evaluate their finished work against the original intention;

Level 1
- talk about what they have done during their designing and making;
- evaluate familiar things by observing and describing them, saying what they like and dislike about them and why people have or need them;

Level 2
- ask people about their preferences;
- recognise that goods are designed, made and distributed;
- recognise a variety of forms resulting from people's different values, cultures, beliefs and needs;
- recognise aesthetic qualities in things around them, and use them in their work;
- recognise that people like certain objects, but not others, find the reason why and use this knowledge in their own designing and appraising;
- talk about what they have learned and what they might do differently next time;

Level 3
- know the importance of exploring needs and opportunities before proposing solutions;
- recognise that a solution may result in problems in other areas;
- consider how well their products are designed and made;
- propose simple modifications to improve the effectiveness of designs and to overcome difficulties when making;
- reflect, individually and in groups, on how they went about their work, and whether changes might be needed.

Planning sheet 1b

Design and technology capability	Programmes of study Key Stage 2
Developing and using artefacts, systems and environments	**Activity**

Core

- organise and plan their work carefully, introducing new ideas, so that their work improves;
- allocate time and other resources effectively throughout the activity;
- control the use of energy to meet design needs;
- use a variety of energy devices;
- plan how practical activities may be organised;
- use a variety of information sources in developing their proposals;
- use knowledge and judgment to make decisions in the light of priorities or constraints;
- identify the parts of a system and their functions, and use this knowledge to inform their designing and making activities;

Level 2

- recognise that control involves making things work as desired;

Level 3

- recognise pattern in the structure of objects;
- know that objects are changed by the forces applied to them;
- know that systems have inputs, processes and outputs and recognise these in a variety of simple systems;
- use simple mechanisms to transfer motion;
- recognise that a source of energy is required to make things work;
- organise their work, taking account of constraints;
- realise that, when working in teams, people may have specialist roles;
- use a variety of energy devices;

Level 4

- make a simple system and consider its effectiveness and whether modifications should be made to the design in order to improve it;
- test simple objects they have made;
- recognise that structures have distinctive characteristics including form and stability;
- use mechanisms to change one type of motion into another;
- recognise that mechanisms need to be controlled if they are to achieve their intended function;
- take into account the characteristics of different energy sources when designing products;
- exercise persistence in their designing and making and recognise when to seek help;
- allocate tasks when leading a team;

Level 5

- recognise that the context of a system involves inputs, outputs, feedback and stability of that system;
- recognise and represent organisational structures;
- select and use simple mechanisms, including linkages and gearing, in making prototypes;
- identify the basic principles of how different mechanisms change speed or change motion, from one form to another;
- recognise that mechanisms can be controlled by computers;
- understand that it may be necessary to practice an operation in order to improve quality;
- take account of the effects of transferring and using energy in their designing and making.

**Planning sheet 1b
continued**

Design and technology capability	Programmes of study Key Stage 2
Working with materials	**Activity**

Core
- use equipment safely;
- select materials for their task;
- rearrange materials to change their strength or character, and to increase their usefulness;
- join materials in semi-permanent forms;
- assemble materials;
- avoid wastage of materials;
- take responsibility for safe working;
- develop co-ordination and control in using equipment;
- finish work carefully;

Level 2
- choose materials and equipment to make objects;
- investigate the properties of materials in the course of their designing and making;
- identify natural and manufactured materials;
- use simple hand tools, and know how to look after them;
- care for their surroundings;

Level 3
- recognise that materials and equipment need to be safely stored and maintained;
- be aware of the dangers of the misuse of materials and equipment, and the consequent risk of accidents;
- use alternative means of joining materials;
- recognise the appropriate tools for working with a variety of materials;

Level 4
- recognise that materials have different working properties;
- recognise the aesthetic qualities of natural and manufactured materials;
- select and use equipment correctly;
- check the condition of equipment before use;

Level 5
- know the working properties of a range of materials;
- recognise the purpose of equipment, to understand the way it works, and to use it;
- identify hazards in the working environment and to take appropriate action if dangerous situations occur.

Developing and communicating ideas

Core
- take account of people's reactions to aesthetic characteristics;
- make the connection between aesthetic characteristics of natural and manufactured objects and relate these to their own work;
- plan and structure their communication of ideas and proposals;
- use drawings and plans to investigate and develop ideas for three-dimensional objects;
- use a range of graphic techniques and processes;
- use modelling to explore design and technological ideas;
- use modelling and recording when generating ideas;
- break design tasks into sub-tasks and focus on each in turn as a way of developing ideas;
- use material and equipment to produce results which are aesthetically pleasing;

Level 2

Level 3
- develop a range of simple skills used in drawing and modelling;

Design and technology capability	Programmes of study Key Stage 2
Level 4	Activity
• make two- or three-dimensional models of their design ideas and to test these before proceeding further; • extend the range of techniques used in their drawing and modelling; • generate ideas and develop them further using a variety of techniques and media; **Level 5** • use specialist vocabulary when communicating proposals; • develop styles of visual communication which take account of what is to be conveyed, the audience and the medium to be used; • present their design and technological ideas and proposals using modelling techniques and specialist vocabulary; • recognise the relationship between two-dimensional representation and three-dimensional forms; • investigate artefacts, system and environments to find ideas for new designs. **Satisfying needs and addressing opportunities** **Core** • know that the needs and preferences of consumers influence the design and production of goods and services; • recognise the importance of consumer choice and hence the importance of product quality and cost; • be aware that the appearance of artefacts and environment is important to consumers and users; • know that human shape, scale, proportion and movement affect the forms of designs; • understand that goods may be designed to be produced singly or in quantity, and that this affects what each item costs; • consider the possible consequences of their design proposals before taking them forward to completion; • consider the needs and values of individuals and of groups, from a variety of backgrounds and cultures; • evaluate at each stage of their work; • make adjustments as a result of evaluation; • use their appraisal of the work of others to help their own work; **Level 2** • ask people about their preferences; • recognise that goods are designed, made and distributed; • recognise a variety of forms resulting from people's different values, cultures, beliefs and needs; • recognise aesthetic qualities in things around them, and use them in their work; • recognise that people like certain objects, but not others, find the reason why and use this knowledge in their own designing and appraising; • talk about what they have learned and what they might do differently next time; **Level 3** • know the importance of exploring needs and opportunities before proposing solutions; • recognise that a solution may result in problems in other areas; • consider how well their products are designed and made; • propose simple modifications to improve the effectiveness of designs and to overcome difficulties when making; • reflect, individually and in groups, on how they went about their work, and whether changes might be needed; **Level 4** • propose modifications to improve the performance and appeal of existing products; • know that advertising helps promote and sell goods and services; • know that costs include time, people, skills, equipment and materials;	

**Planning sheet 1b
continued**

Design and technology capability	Programmes of study Key Stage 2
	Activity
• make judgments about products designed and made by others; • evaluate the outcome of their activity against the original need, and propose modifications that would improve the overall quality of the outcome; • reflect on how they went about a task and how they might plan their next task differently; **Level 5** • identify markets for goods and services; • know that, in the production and distribution of goods, the control of stock is important; • plan a simple budget; • investigate the effects of design and technological activity on the environment; • establish and apply criteria for assessing the needs and opportunities identified, the choice of materials and equipment to achieve the design procedures adopted, the end result.	

Planning sheet 2a

Key Stage 1 Core						Level 1						
Majority of activities will cover: Pupils should be taught to: • use imagination, and their own experiences, to generate and explore ideas; • represent and develop ideas by drawings, models, talking, writing, working with materials; • find out, sort, store and present information for use in designing and making. • identify what should be done and ways in which work should be organised. • realise that resources are limited, and choices must be made; • evaluate their finished work against the original intention.						• talk about what they have done during their designing and making.						
Most activities will cover: Pupils should be taught to: • explore and use a variety of materials to make and design things; • recognise that materials are processed in order to change or control their properties; • recognise that many materials are available and have different characteristics which make them appropriate for different tasks; • join materials and components in simple ways; • use materials and equipment safely.												
Some activities will cover: Pupils should be taught to: • know that a system is made of related parts which are combined for a purpose; • identify the jobs done by parts of a system; • give a sequence of instructions to produce a desired result; • recognise, and make models of, simple structures around them; • use sources of energy to make things move; • know that goods are bought, sold and advertised.						• make simple objects for a purpose. • recognise that materials can be linked in various ways to make or allow movement. • evaluate familiar things by observing and describing them, saying what they like or dislike about them and why people have or need them.						

Level 2							Level 3							
							• develop a range of simple skills used in drawing and modelling.							
							• organise their work, taking account of constraints; • realise that, when working in teams, people may have specialist roles.							
• talk about what they have learned and what they might do differently next time.							• know the importance of exploring needs and opportunities before proposing solutions; • recognise that a solution may result in problems in other areas; • consider how well their products are designed and made; • propose simple modifications to improve the effectiveness of designs and to overcome difficulties when making; • reflect, individually and in groups, on how they went about their work, and whether changes might be needed.							
• choose materials and equipment to make objects; • investigate the properties of materials in the course of their designing and making; • identify natural and manufactured materials.							• use alternative means of joining materials; • recognise the appropriate tools for working with a variety of materials.							
• use simple hand tools, and know how to look after them; • care for their surroundings.							• recognise that materials and equipment need to be safely stored and maintained; • be aware of the dangers of the misuse of materials and equipment, and the consequent risk of accidents.							
• recognise that control involves making things work as desired.							• know that systems have inputs, processes and outputs and recognise these in a variety of simple systems; • recognise pattern in the structure of objects; • know that objects are changed by the forces applied to them.							
• recognise that goods are designed, made and distributed; • recognise a variety of forms resulting from people's different values, cultures, beliefs and needs; • recognise aesthetic qualities in things around them, and use them in their work; • ask people about their preferences; • recognise that people like certain objects, but not others, find the reason why and use this knowledge in their own designing and appraising.							• use a variety of energy devices. • recognise that a source of energy is required to make things work; • use simple mechanisms to transfer motion.							

Planning sheet 2b

Key Stage 2 Core	Level 4
Majority of activities will cover: Pupils should be taught to: • organise and plan their work carefully, introducing new ideas, so that their work improves; • allocate time and other resources effectively throughout the activity; • plan how practical activities may be organised; • use a variety of information sources in developing their proposals; • use knowledge and judgment to make decisions in the light of priorities or constraints; • take account of people's reactions to aesthetic characteristics; • make the connections between aesthetic characteristics of natural and manufactured objects and relate these to their own work; • plan and structure their communication of ideas and proposals; • use drawings and plans to investigate and develop ideas for three-dimensional objects; • use a range of graphic techniques and processes; • use modelling to explore design and technological ideas; • use modelling and recording when generating ideas; • break design tasks into sub-tasks and focus on each in turn as a way of developing ideas; • use materials and equipment to produce results which are aesthetically pleasing; • consider the possible consequences of their design proposals before taking them forward to completion; • consider the needs and values of individuals and of groups, from a variety of backgrounds and cultures; • evaluate at each stage of their work; • make adjustments as a result of evaluation; • use their appraisal of the work of others to help their own work.	• make two- or three dimensional models of their design ideas and to test these before proceeding further; • extend the range of techniques used in their drawing and modelling; • generate ideas and develop them further variety of techniques and media. • reflect on how they went about a task, and how they might plan their next task differently. • evaluate the outcome of their activity against the original need, and propose modifications that would improve the overall quality of the outcome; • exercise persistence in their designing and making and recognise when to seek help; • allocate tasks when leading a team.
Most activities will cover: Pupils should be taught to: • use equipment safely; • select materials for their task; • take responsibility for safe working; • develop co-ordination and control in using equipment; • rearrange materials to change their strength or character, and to increase their usefulness; • join materials in semi-permanent forms; • assemble materials; • avoid wastage of materials; • finish work carefully.	• check the condition of equipment before use. • select and use equipment correctly; • recognise the purpose of equipment, to understand the way it works, and to use it; • identify hazards in the working environment and to take appropriate action if dangerous situations occur. • recognise that materials have different working properties; • know the working properties of a range of materials; • recognise the aesthetic qualities of natural and manufactured materials.
Some activities will cover: Pupils should be taught to: • identify the parts of a system and their functions, and use this knowledge to inform their designing and making activities; • control the use of energy to meet design needs; • use a variety of energy devices; • know that the needs and preferences of consumers influence the design and production of goods and services; • recognise the importance of consumer choice and hence the importance of product quality and cost; • be aware that the appearance of artefacts and environments is important to consumers and users; • know that human shape, scale, proportion and movement affect the forms of designs; • understand that goods may be designed to be produced singly or in quantity, and that this affects what each item costs.	• make a simple system and consider its effectiveness and whether modifications should be made to the design in order to improve it; • test simple objects they have made; • recognise that structures have distinctive characteristics including form and stability; • take into account the characteristics of different energy sources when designing products; • use mechanisms to change one type of motion into another; • recognise that mechanisms need to be controlled if they are to achieve their intended function; • propose modifications to improve the performance and appeal of existing products; • know that advertising helps promote and sell goods and services; • know that costs include time, people, skills, equipment and materials; • make judgments about products designed and made by others.

Level 5	
• use specialist vocabulary when communicating proposals; • develop styles of visual communication which take account of what is to be conveyed, the audience and the medium to be used; • present their design and technological ideas and proposals using modelling techniques and specialist vocabulary; • recognise the relationships between two-dimensional representation and three-dimensional forms; • investigate artefacts, systems and environments to find ideas for new designs. • establish and apply criteria for assessing: the needs and opportunities identified; the choice of materials and equipment to achieve the design; the procedures adopted; the end result.	
• recognise that the control of a system involves inputs, outputs, feedback and stability of that system; • recognise and represent organisational structures; • take account of the effects of transferring and using energy in their designing and making. • select and use simple mechanisms, including linkages and gearing in making prototypes; • identify the basic principles of how different mechanisms change speed or change motion, from one form to another; • recognise that it may be necessary to practice an operation in order to improve quality; • know that, in the production and distribution of goods, the control of stock is important; • plan a simple budget; • investigate the effects of design and technological activity on the environment.	

Progression sheet 1

Programmes of study Developing and using artefacts, systems and environment	Key Stages 1 and 2		Aspects of progression		
	Key Stage 1		Key Stage 2		
	L1		L3		L5
Artefacts	Make models of simple structures	Include parts that move; have a purpose for the model	Recognise; Control e.g. movement of model	Know objects can be changed by force	Know objects have form and stability
Systems	Understand systems are made of parts and identify them	Know a system has inputs, processes, outputs	Make a system and evaluate it		
Mechanisms		Use simple mechanisms (in a ready made artefact)	Use mechanism to transfer one type of motion to another e.g. cam, lever; understand need for control		Use, understand & control by computers
Energy	Use sources of energy to make things move	Use different sources of energy. Use a variety of devices	Choose right energy source for a particular model. Control energy		
Organising the work		Take account of constraints. Work in teams, identify specialist roles	Organise & plan work. Use a variety of information sources. Allocate time, resources during the activity		Show an ability to allocate tasks as a team leader. Perseverance

Progression sheet 2

Working with materials

	Key Stage 1		Key Stage 2	
	L1	L3		L5
Equipment	Use safely	Learn to use, choose, look after tools; Keep working area tidy and clean	Learn to store equipment safely; Be aware of the dangers and misuse of tools	Check before use; Understand the purpose for and way that equipment works; Be aware of potential hazards in the working environment
Materials	Use and explore a variety of materials e.g. fabric, card, paper, wood, clay, dough, paint; Realise materials have different properties; Join in simple ways	Choose materials; Investigate their properties, including natural and man-made material	Avoid wastage; Finish work carefully; Find alternative ways of joining	Understand the working properties of a range of materials

Developing and communicating ideas

	L1	L3	Key Stage 2	L5
Developing ideas	Draw on own experiences and imagination	Plan and structure ideas, using drawings & plans for 3D objects;	Develop ideas further by use of variety of techniques & media	Use specialist vocabulary; Investigate existing artefacts, systems & environments; Recognise relationship between 2D representation and 3D form
Communicating ideas	Use e.g. talking, writing, models, drawings	Use modelling to convey ideas	Use techniques e.g. plans, templates, patterns, flow diagrams	Use specialist vocabulary; Think about different styles for visual communication
Use of IT	Find out, store, sort present information for a design and technology activity	Use range of simple skills used in drawing, sketching, scale models, measurement	Use a range of graphic techniques and processes	Use specialist vocabulary

Progression sheet 3

Satisfying needs and addressing opportunities	Key Stage 1		Key Stage 2
	L1	**L3**	**L5**
Explore needs & opportunities		Need to do this before proposing solutions; Understand solutions may lead to other problems	
Goods – design and consumer choice	Know that goods are bought, sold and advertised	Find out about preferences and reasons for them e.g. different values, beliefs, cultures, needs	Advertising helps to sell goods. Think about appearance, cost, quality, shape, scale, human form & how it affects preferences Identify a market for the goods
Resources	Resources are limited and choices must be made		
Economic considerations		Cost depends on production – single/multiple – quality	Cost includes: time, people, skills, equipment, material Plan a simple budget
Evaluation	Evaluate against original intention	What did they learn? What could they do better?	Evaluate: – organisation – working in groups – product – designing, making, modifying Evaluate: – task – how might it be planned next time? – other products

Software progression sheet

An example of the way in which schools can record a balanced and progressive software policy. (The programs are only indicative; schools would, of course, choose those that are appropriate for their own needs.)

	R	Y1	Y2	Y3	Y4	Y5	Y6
Communicating information	Window →	Paint pot →					
		Paint →					
		Minnie →					
		Caxton →					
			Writeon →				
			Write →				
			Frontpage extra →				
Handling information	Data show →		Ourfacts →				
			Sorting game →				
			Branch →				
Modelling		Lost frog →		Granny's Garden →		Suburban Fox →	
				Dragon's World →			
Measurement & control			First Sense →	Turtle graphics →			
				Logo →			
						Control logo →	
					Grasshopper →	Grass →	

7
Assessment and record-keeping

Perhaps this is the issue, above all others, that has generated the most debate, misunderstanding and disagreement. Indeed, as with other curricular areas, there are both general and particular considerations that need to be discussed.

General considerations

1. The purposes of assessment are similar across the whole curriculum:
   - Assessment should be formative, in order to provide teachers with information to assist them in making their daily and weekly decisions concerning individual pupils. This will be part of the continuous teacher assessment (also known as continuous and/or internal assessment) that takes place over part of a term, year and key stage.
   - Assessment should be summative, in order to provide an overview of the pupils' achievement over a longer period of time (such as a whole term, year or key stage).
   - Assessment should be evaluative, in order to help identify both strengths and areas where changes may be needed.
   - Assessment should be informative and recorded in a way that is most likely to be of use to any interested parties.
2. There may be standard assessment tasks that involve the assessment of design and technology capability. Although the nature of these tasks has not yet been clarified, it is likely that the SATs will link a number of curriculum areas and will be non-statutory.
3. An attempt should be made to devise records that are accessible yet reasonably comprehensive.

Particular considerations

1. There is no sharply defined body of knowledge that has to be assessed (the term 'know that' is used only once and the term 'understand that' only twice within the statements of attainment for both Key Stages 1 and 2).
2. There is an explicit emphasis on dialogue and interaction between all those who are involved in the assessment which is shown by the continuous use of terms such as 'describe', 'express', 'show', 'discuss', and 'comment'.

3. There is a need to assess the child's involvement in the holistic process (all four attainment targets) through one activity. Individual processes (attainment targets) cannot be assessed through different activities.
4. There is a need to assess information technology capability during design and technology activities.
5. There are numerous, generalised statements of attainment that are open to a variety of interpretations. Examples include 'a range of', 'make choices' and 'make judgments'.

Implications

What are the implications raised by these considerations for assessment of design and technology activities?

1. The phrase 'use knowledge' in the statements of attainment highlights the need for children to gain, or to have, the necessary skills to attain appropriate knowledge at different levels. For example, at level 4 in the programmes of study, it is suggested that children may draw on their understanding of levers or cams. It would therefore be valuable to have already introduced work related to these mechanisms during science orientated sessions.
2. The emphasis on oral communication implies that children who have problems with that form of communication should not be disadvantaged unduly; there must be adequate time allowed for group discussion or for any other appropriate form of communication that is to be used; and there must be provision of time for discussion on a one-to-one basis to allow the child to communicate in a non-threatening situation.
3. It may be difficult to manage the assessment of an entire class involved in one activity, especially if there is only one adult available. However, if different groups are assessed during different activities, there may be an imbalance in the assessed work. Careful pre-planning of possible contexts, resources and outcomes in order to ensure breadth and balance of assessed activities is essential.
4. It will be necessary to decide if records for information technology capability and design and technology capability assessment should be kept separately or combined together to form a technology assessment.
5. It will be necessary to decide upon an understanding of generalised statements through discussions with the whole staff and/or with an external body or bodies. The latter may include cluster groups, advisory teachers, advisors and inspectors. (Attendance at local, regional and national conferences would of course help the process of moderation of ideas.) Eventually, guidance on this issue may even be forthcoming from NCC.) This understanding could be linked to the idea of 'levelness'. Staff would have discussed and gained an overview of all the level statements across

the four attainment targets to ensure they have a common view of what each level will 'look like'. This is, of course, a simplistic view, but it is one that could be used as a starting point.

Assessment strategies

What strategies can be used when assessing the children?

The strategies that are used for design and technology capability are similar to those used for other curriculum areas, but the emphasis may be different. These strategies include:

— the questioning of the children during each stage of the activity;
— the use of peer group observations;
— the use of concrete evidence in the form of, for example, drawings, sketches, models, tape recordings, computer print-outs and written communication;
— the close observation of the children while they are engaged in the activities. This may include their handling of materials and tools; watching their interaction with other group members; and listening to their conversations with peers, other adults and the teacher.

How can such evidence be recorded?

To keep a record of daily observations, a notebook, acting as a diary, is one tried and tested method used by many teachers. To record assessment made over longer periods of time, schools need to draw up their own record sheets. As it is unlikely that any one method will suit all schools, it is intended that the following suggestions should form a basis upon which to draw.

A wheel

This type of sheet has been used for recording for all key stages, both before and after the introduction of the National Curriculum (see p.63)

Considerations:

— the differing levels can be seen clearly;
— if statements are added to each segment, it is hard to read them once the record sheet is filled in;
— if statements are not added, there is no information on the sheet as to the meaning of the levels of achievement;
— there is no space for pupil/teacher comments.

Pupil/teacher comment charts

Considerations:

- the differing levels can be seen clearly;
- if one sheet is used for each activity, it could generate large quantities of paperwork but there is room for some pupil/teacher comments;
- if one sheet is used for a number of activities (a year or key stage), there is little room for pupil/teacher comments.

(See p.64)

AT checklists

Considerations:

- the differing levels can be seen clearly;
- it is easy to indicate specific links with other curriculum areas;
- there is no room for pupil/teacher comments.

(See p.66)

IT record sheet

Considerations:

- the sheet can be used for design and technology activities;
- the sheet can be used for all curriculum areas.

(See p.68)

Summative pupil/teacher comment sheet

An additional sheet could be added to allow for summative pupil/ teacher comments and for the recording of a range of tools and materials that have been used.

(See p.69)

Identifying progress

What are the main strands showing progression which can be identified within the attainment targets?

The Document has identified the following:

AT1

Level 2 Suggest changes, ask questions

Level 3 Identify needs and opportunities, clarify ideas

Level 4 Unfamiliar situations, other peoples' points of view, conflicting criteria, justifying their conclusions, the past and other cultures

Level 5 Economic, social, environmental considerations

AT2

Level 2 Give simple reasons for choosing their design

Level 3 Make a design proposal, choose from their ideas, use models to develop their design, record how they have explored different ideas

Level 4 Review their design proposals, estimate resource requirements and check availability

Level 5 Record the progress of their ideas, seek to organise information, adapt designs to take account of resources, use simple plans and flow diagrams

AT3

Level 2 Use simple hand tools, materials and components, use working knowledge of characteristics of materials

Level 3 Constraints of time and availability of resources, have some regard for accuracy and quality, improvise when difficulties arise

Level 4 Minimise waste, work with others – division of labour recognise when help is needed, use diagrams and drawings

Level 5 Identify stages in making, produce a simple plan

AT4

Level 2 Products from other times and cultures

Level 3 Considering the needs of other, commenting on materials used, reviewing how the task was tackled;

Level 4 Justifying decisions, understanding social and economic implications

Level 5 Indicating improvements; evaluating against the original needs

Assessment wheel

Name
D of B
School

Suggested code for completion
✔ each time experienced/covered. Shade
when it is felt competency has been achieved

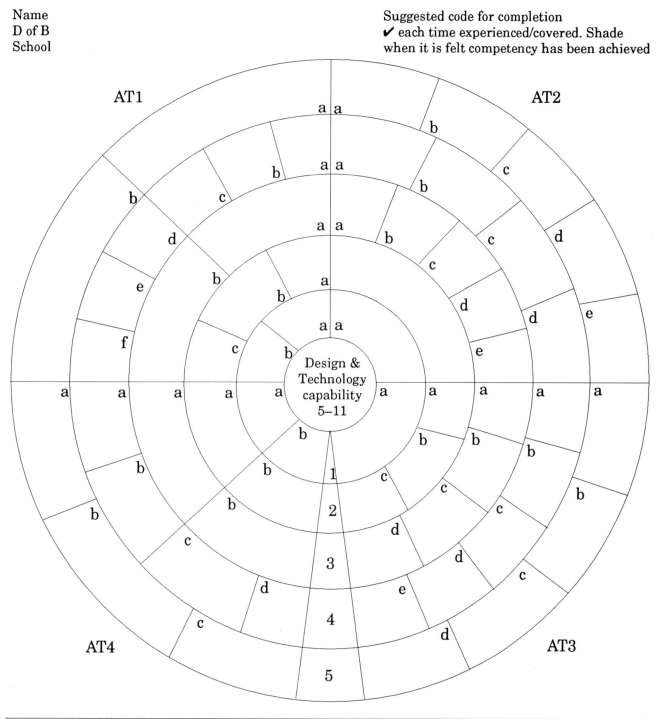

Year	R	Y1	Y2	Y3	Y4	Y5	Y6	Year	R	Y1	Y2	Y3	Y4	Y5	Y6
Outcome								**Context**							
Artefact								Home							
System								School							
Environment								Recreation							
Tick each time product produced								Community							
								Business & industry							
								Tick each time a context is experienced							

Pupil/teacher comment chart

Name / Year	R	Y1	Y2	Y3	Y4	Y5	Y6
Outcome							
Artefact							
System							
Environment							

D of B

Year / Context	R	Y1	Y2	Y3	Y4	Y5	Y6
Home							
School							
Recreation							
Community							
Business & industry							

School

	Experienced ✔ each time	Competent shade & date	Pupil comment	Teacher comment
AT1 1a				
b				
2a				
b				
c				
3a				
b				
4a				
b				
c				
d				
e				
f				
5a				
b				
AT2 1a				
2a				
3a				
b				
c				
d				
e				
4a				

b	c	d	5a	b	c	d	e	1a	2a	b	c	3a	b	c	d	4a	b	c	d	e	5a	b	c	d	1a	b	2a	b	3a	b	4a	b	c	d	5a	b	c
								AT 3																	AT 4												

AT checklist

AT1 Identifying needs and opportunities	AT2 Generating a design	AT3 Planning and making	AT4 Evaluating	AT5 Information Technology capability
Pupils should be able to identify and state clearly needs and opportunities for design and technological activities through investigations of the contexts of home, school, recreation community, business and industry.	Pupils should be able to generate a design specification, explore ideas to produce a design proposal and develop it into a realistic, appropriate and achieveable design.	Pupils should be able to make artefacts, systems and environments, preparing and working to a plan and identifying, managing and using appropriate resources, including knowledge and processes.	Pupils should be able to develop, communicate, and act upon an evaluation of the processes, products and effects of their design and technological activities and of those of others, including those from other times and cultures.	
Pupils should be able to:	Pupils should be able to:	Pupils should be able to:	Pupils should be able to:	Pupils should be able to:
1a) describe to others what they have noticed in familiar surroundings or visualised about imaginary situations.	1a) express their ideas about what they might do to meet an identified need or opportunity.	1a) use a variety of materials and equipment to make simple things.	1a) describe to others what they have done and how well they have done it.	1a) work with a computer.
1b) suggest what might be done			1b) describe to others what they like and dislike about familiar artefacts, systems or environments.	1b) talk about ways in which equipment, such as toys and domestic appliances, responds to signals or commands.
2a) describe what they have observed or visualised and found out in their exploration.	2a) use talk, pictures, drawings, models, to develop their design proposals, giving simple reasons why they have chosen to make their design.	2a) describe to others how they are going about their work.	2a) discuss with teachers and others how satisfied they are with their designs and technological activities, taking into account their original intention and how they went about their task.	2a) use computer-generated pictures, symbols, words or phrases to communicate meaning.
2b) suggest practical changes that could be made in response to a need and describe to others why they suggested certain changes.		2b) use knowledge of the working characteristics of materials and components, including construction kits, in making artefacts, systems or environments.		2b) use information technology for the storage and retrieval of information.
2c) ask questions which help them to identify needs and opportunities for design and technological activity.		2c) show that they can use simple hand tools, materials and components.	2b) make simple judgments about familiar artefacts, systems or environments, including those from other times and cultures.	
3a) starting with a familiar situation, use their knowledge and the results of investigations to identify needs and opportunities for design and technological activity.	3a) make a design proposal by selecting from their ideas and giving reasons for their choices.	3a) consider constraints of time and availability of resources in planning and making.	3a) discuss their design and technological activities and their outcomes with teachers and others, taking into account how well they have met the needs of others.	3a) use information technology to make, amend and present information.
	3b) apply knowledge and skills to select ideas for different parts of their design.	3b) choose resources for making by using their knowledge of the characteristics of materials and components.		3b) give a sequence of direct instructions to control movement.
	3c) draw from information about materials, people, markets and processes and from other times and cultures to help in developing their ideas.	3c) use a range of hand tools and equipment appropriate to the materials and components with some regard for accuracy and quality.	3b) comment on the materials and processes used and how the task was tackled.	3c) collect information and enter it in a database (whose structure may have been prepared in advance), and to select and retrieve information from the database.
3b) develop and clarify their ideas about possible needs and opportunities	3d) use models including annotated drawings and three-dimensional working models to develop their design.			3d) describe their use of information technology and compare it with other methods.
	3e) record how they have explored different ideas about a design and			4a) use information technology to retrieve, develop, organise and present work.

through discussion with those involved.

4a) starting with an unfamiliar situation, identify needs and opportunities for design and technological activity.

4b) devise ways of gathering information in addition to using printed sources.

4c) recognise the points of view of others and consider what it is like to be in another person's situation.

4d) explain that a range of criteria which are sometimes conflicting must be used to make judgments about what is worth doing.

4e) provide oral and written justification for the conclusions they reach as a result of investigation.

4f) know that in the past and in other cultures people have used design and technology to solve familiar problems in different ways.

5a) show judgment in the choice of sources of information, both qualitative and quantative, in the systematic search for a need or opportunity for a design and technological activity.

5b) recognise that economic, social, environmental and technological considerations and the preferences of users are important in developing opportunites.

---

technological proposal to see how realistic it might be.

4a) record their ideas as they develop.

4b) review their design proposal to identify where decisions still need to be made, suggest possible courses of action which will improve their proposal.

4c) estimate the resource requirements and check on availability.

4d) describe and edit design proposals.

5a) record the progress of their ideas, showing how they have clarified and developed them.

5b) extend their first ideas by combining various aspects of them to formulate a design proposal and explain why some ideas were not used.

5c) seek out and organise information to help them develop their ideas and refine their design proposal.

5d) establish and check the availability of the resources required, adapting their design as appropriate.

5e) specify what they intend to do and what they will need by using simple plans and flow diagrams.

3d) improvise within the limits of materials, resources and skills when faced with unforeseen difficulties.

4a) adopt procedures which minimise waste, pay regard to cost and achieve accuracy and finish.

4b) work with others in the planning an apportioning of tasks.

4c) choose tools, equipment and processes suitable for making their design and use these appropriately.

4d) adopt alternative ways of carrying forward their plan when difficulties are encountered and recognise when help is needed.

4e) use drawings, diagrams and three-dimensional models, to assist making.

5a) identify stages in making and coordinate these into a simple plan to ensure efficient use of time, materials and labour.

5b) use knowledge and understanding of the properties of a range of materials in their planning and making.

5c) demonstrate by their choice and use of a variety of equipment that they understand the principles upon which these work and the requirements of safety and accuracy.

5d) apply knowledge of materials, components and processes to overcome problems in making as these arise.

4a) review the ways in which their design has developed during the activity, justifying decisions and appraising results in relation to intentions.

4b) review the decision-making process they used in producing their final artefact, system or environment

4c) comment upon existing artefacts, systems or environments, and those from other times and cultures, including appearance and use of resources.

4d) understand the social and economic implications of some artefacts, systems or environments.

5a) evaluate their product in relation to the design intentions and to the original needs or opportunities, taking into account users' views, cost-effectiveness and scale of production.

5b) justify the ideas, materials, components, procedures, techniques and processes used and indicate possible improvements.

5c) understand that artefacts, systems or environments from other times and cultures have identifiable characteristics and styles, and draw upon this knowledge in design and technological activities.

4b) develop a set of commands to control the movement of a screen image or robot; understand that a computer program or procedure is a set of instructions to be followed in a pre-determined sequence.

4c) amend and add to information in an existing database, to check its plausibility and interrogate it.

4d) understand the need to question the accuracy of displayed information and that results produced by a computer may be affected by incorrect data entry.

4e) use a computer model to detect patterns and relationships, and how the rules governing the model work.

4f) review their experience of information technology and consider applications in everyday life.

5a) use information technology to present information in different forms for specific purposes.

5b) understand that a computer can control devices by a series of commands, and appreciate the need for precision in framing commands.

5c) use a software package to create a computer database so that data can be captured, stored and retrieved.

5d) use information technology to explore patterns and relationships, and to form and test simple hypotheses.

5e) understand that personal information may be held on computer, which is of interest to themselves and their families.

IT record sheet

either – use in conjunction with design and technology record sheet
or – use for all curricular areas
Fill in – programme used
– date

Indicate when competent

	R	Year 1	Year 2	Year 3	Year 4	Year 5	Year 6
Communicating information							
Handling information							
Modelling							
Measurement and control							

Summative pupil/teacher comment sheet

Name
D of B
School

AT1	AT2
AT3	**AT4**

Range of tools

Range of materials	
Textiles	
Artists' media	
Food	
Construction materials	

Part C
Design and technology in practice

8
Content

While the programmes of study outline the content to be covered, it has been open to schools to develop their own methods of covering this content in a balanced and appropriate way. A mixture of the following three methods has proved successful in a variety of schools and could be adapted and used by others. This has involved using:

- everyday opportunities;
- special occasions/projects;
- topic work.

Whatever method is used, consideration should be given to the following:

- a broad and balanced coverage of content throughout each key stage;
- a variety of outcomes (artefact, system, environment);
- a variety of contexts, possibly starting with the familiar;
- progression;
- equal opportunities.

Everyday opportunities
Using everyday opportunities for design and technology activities may prove particularly appropriate for:

- young children and children with special educational needs because they will provide a variety of short, 'concrete' activities, set in relevant situations;
- covering a particular 'gap' in the programmes of study for a group of children;

Special projects
Using special projects for design and technology activities may prove particularly appropriate for:

- covering a particular 'gap' in the programmes of study, e.g. economic awareness;
- involving the children in a particular school event;
- providing a focus for liaison work.

Topic work

Providing the topics are broad, they should offer a wide range of opportunities from which design and technology activities can be developed.

The suggested activity planning sheet on p.76 should be sufficiently open-ended to overcome the difficulty of explaining an activity (in writing) without being prescriptive.

Suggestions for ways in which design and technology activities could be developed are given in the activity planning and development sheets (pp.77–114). They are not related to a key stage because it is felt that teachers can adapt the ideas to suit the stage at which their children are operating (differentiation by outcome and not task). Nor are the starting points fixed – children could start at various stages in the design and technology process. However, it is intended to show that design and technology activities may arise from a variety of real and imaginary situations; that children should learn to work together; that children should be able to use a range of materials and equipment; and that children should have the opportunity to develop such qualities as creativity and independence.

Practical skills and techniques

While the programmes of study outline in broad terms the practical skills to be covered, they contain little to indicate precisely what should be included other than the few examples offered alongside the programmes of study in the National Curriculum document itself. Not surprisingly, this has resulted in a wide variety of opinion as to what should be included according, it seems, to the backgrounds and interests of local INSET providers, advisory teachers and individual teachers.

Moreover, there are differing opinions as to what is realistic at the different key stages. But these must surely be dependent upon the children's previous experiences, the availability of equipment, and the practical skills and confidence of the teacher, all of which, at the present time, may be somewhat limited. However, as children come to experience more structured work developing design and technology capability, as schools build up resources, and as teachers gain confidence, the children's range of practical skills and techniques will no doubt be considerably extended.

The practical skills and techniques sheets (pp.115–131) illustrate a possible core of these skills and techniques. It would be impossible to divide them rigidly between Key Stages 1 and 2, and it is expected that individual schools will add to, take out, reorganise and prioritise those which are suitable for their own children.

Whatever practical skills and techniques schools decide to include, there are certain general issues to consider:

- the variety of practical skills offered by different curriculum areas – there has been considerable emphasis (some would say an over-emphasis) placed on skill development in the area which traditionally has been known as CDT;
- the stages by which progression can be achieved;
- the objectives which the children can realistically achieve;
- the range of equipment and materials that will be needed;
- the methods of teaching that will most effectively encompass the range of skills and techniques to be covered. Two suggested methods are:
  - on an 'as and when it is appropriate' basis
  - through a teacher-directed task;
- the provision of staff INSET to increase awareness and personal skills.

Activity planning sheet (outline)

Theme/topic:

Activity:

Setting the context (putting the children in the picture)	**Possible contexts**
	Home Community
	School Business
	Recreation & industry

	Possible outcomes
Particular resources, equipment	Artefact
	System
	Environment

	IT links

Possible development:

Everyday projects development sheet 1

Everyday opportunities	Development	Possible outcomes
Deliveries around the school (including messages, milk, dinner numbers, notices, post) **Possible contexts:** School Community	Evaluation of present systems. What particular problems are encountered? **Some points that could be considered:** Different routes may be needed for different purposes; different artefacts may be useful in assisting delivery or passing on information. **Evaluation:** Is it better? – faster, more accurate information, easier to move . . .	System Artefact
Fire drill **Possible contexts:** School Community	Are there any problems at present? Try present system out. **Some points that could be considered:** Position of suggested exit doors; even distribution of children passing through each door; position of children away from school; access to fire regulations; readability of regulations **Evaluation:** Is the new system better? Does everyone know what to do? Is the school emptied more quickly? Are there any other improvements that could be made?	System Artefact

Everyday projects development sheet 2

Everyday opportunities	Development	Possible outcomes
Putting out/away of large PE apparatus **Possible contexts:** School Recreation Community	Evaluation of present system. **Some points that could be considered:** Position of apparatus in relation to storage points; waiting point for children not involved in moving the apparatus; safety aspects; does everyone know what to do? **Evaluation:** Is the apparatus put out/away faster? Is it done safely? Has it been put away tidily? What improvements could still be made?	System
Arrangment of PE apparatus **Possible contexts:** School Recreation Community	Evaluation of present arrangement. **Some points that could be considered:** Is it safe to get on and off the apparatus? Do children bump into each other? Is the arrangement varied, interesting? **Evaluation:** Are exits/entrances to apparatus spaced out? Does the arrangement provide an interesting circuit? Is the arrangement suitable for a variety of age groups (if appropriate)?	Environment

Everyday projects development sheet 3

Everyday opportunities	Development	Possible outcomes
Visitors to the school	Is it easy for a visitor to find his/her way into and around the school? Evaluate by asking visitors.	System
Possible contexts: School Community	**Some points that could be considered:** Can the school name board be clearly seen from the road? Is the entrance clearly marked? Is the reception area identified? Do present 'routing arrows' show whole routes (or leave halfway round the route)? Are classes, library etc, clearly marked? Are labels written in appropriate languages?	Artefact
	Evaluation: Ask visitors to compare new and old systems. Ask new visitors if system is clear. What changes are needed? What modifications could still be made?	
Improving the environment inside	Do visitors find the environment welcoming? Do the children feel attracted to different areas in the school? What improvements could be made?	Environment
e.g. front entrance, hall, dining hall, cloakroom areas, corridors	**Some points that could be considered:** How could walls be improved? What kind of displays would prove most interesting? What might visitors need while they wait in the entrance? What could be done to make areas tidy and 'sweet smelling'? How could draughts be excluded?	Artefact(s)
	Evaluation: Ask visitors, children for their opinions. Do they feel the area/s are more welcoming? What else could be achieved?	

Everyday projects development sheet 4

Everyday opportunities	Development	Possible outcomes
Outside School garden, playground **Possible contexts:** School Community	These could be short- or long-term projects. **Short term** – possibilities include clearing litter, repositioning bins, furniture, clearing flowerbeds, putting edging stones round grass, sand pit, planting established bushes, plants **Long term** – possibilities include developing a garden (herb, wildlife, vegetable . . .) making and planting tubs, creating and painting games on the playground. **Evaluation:** Looking at photos, asking visitors, asking children – does it look more attractive? Is wildlife attracted to the area?	Environment Artefact(s)
Establishing general rules for school, playground behaviour **Possible contexts:** School Community	Do we need rules? How do they help? Why have rules? What do the children consider important? Evaluate any present school rules. **Some points that could be considered:** Who should make the rules? What rules are needed? How are they going to be publicised? How are they to be enforced? Should there be a code of conduct rather than rules? **Evaluation:** How is the system working? Are people happy with it? What happens if the rules are broken? What could be done to improve the system?	System Artefact(s)

Special projects development sheet 1

Special projects	Development	Possible outcomes
Fund-raising event e.g. jumble sale; Christmas/summer fair; environmental issue; national appeal **Possible contexts:** School Community Business/industry	Evaluation of past events both in and out of school. **Some points that could be considered**: What sells well? What stalls? How many stalls? What is the best time, date, place for the event? What preparations are needed before the day What will need to be done on the day and after the event? How will it be publicised? What special attractions should be included (e.g. Father Christmas)? How much should be charged for entrance, programme, goods? How will the work involved in organising the event be divided? What will each class do? **Evaluation**: Was the event well attended? Was a profit made? How could it have been improved?	System Artefact(s)
Special event e.g. Sports day Open day **Possible contexts:** School Recreation Community	Evaluation of past events **Some points that could be considered**: What is the best time, date, place for the event? Who should be invited? What kind of activities/races? Is there a balance to enable all to take part? What preparations before the day, on the day, after the event? How will it be publicised? Should there be prizes? How will/would non-prize winners react? **Evaluation**: Did it 'run smoothly'? Did everyone enjoy themselves? Was everyone involved? Were the events varied? Was it interesting to watch? How could it be improved?	System Artefact(s)

Special projects development sheet 2

Special projects	Development	Possible outcomes
Play, concert, puppet show	Evaluate own experiences. **Some points that could be considered:** Reason for concert/play – will it raise money? Where will the money go? Is it part of topic work? What type of performance – musical, sketches, whole play? Who will be involved (whole school, class, year group)? How will the work be distributed? Who will do each part? How will it be publicised? **Evaluation:** Did the performance run smoothly? Did the audience enjoy it? How could this information be gathered? Did the participants enjoy it? Would anything be done differently next time?	System Artefact Environment
Party or celebration **Possible contexts:** Home School Recreation Community	Reason for the celebration; evaluate own experiences. (This may provide an opportunity for research into cultures other than their own.) **Some points that could be considered:** What type of food, entertainment, decorations will be needed? What time, date, place? Who will be invited? Who will make the invitations? Who will make and/or buy food? **Evaluation:** Did the participants enjoy themseves? Did everyone take part? Was there sufficient food? Were there enough/too many games? Did everyone know the correct time and place? What changes next time?	System Artefact Environment

Special projects development sheet 3

Special projects	Development	Possible outcomes
Day visit/ Residential visit **Possible contexts:** School Recreation Community	Are the children really involved in their visit(s)? **Some points that could be considered:** Where will the children go? What is the purpose of the visit? What needs to be done – time, date to fix; book transport; determine the route to be taken; decide what to take e.g. food, clothes, first aid equipment; research area/place to be visited; cost visit; inform parents; collection of money; involvement of other adults; make-up of groups/pairs. **Evaluation:** What modifications were needed? Was it enjoyable? What was learned? What would be needed next time?	System
Links with factory/ shop/ bank/ farm **Possible contexts:** Community Business/industry	This may result in the creation of a production line/shop back in school. **Some points that could be considered:** Where will the project be set up? What will be made? How will it be costed? What purpose has the end product? How will the product be sold? How will the product be advertised? **Evaluation:** How did the team work on the production line? Did the product sell well? Was the advertising successful? What could they do differently next time?	System

Special projects development sheet 4

Special projects	Development	Possible outcomes
Promoting the school; feeling part of a community **Possible contexts:** School Community Business/industry	Opportunity to encourage children to develop a sense of pride, belonging to a school. **Some points that could be considered:** What kind of things promote a sense of belonging? – e.g. newsletter, logo, improving environment both inside/outside, participation of parents in school life. What could be done? How will the work be divided up? **Evaluation:** Do the children feel a greater sense of belonging? Do they value what goes on in school? Do parents, visitors, governors, feel part of the community? Do they feel informed?	Artefact Environment System
Conservation of resources **Possible contexts:** Home School Community Business/industry	Opportunity to increase the children's awareness of the importance of the conservation of our resources. Some points that could be considered: what items de we throw away that could be re-used? – e.g. plastic bags, odd buttons, packets. What could be done to encourage people to re-use them? e.g. collections at school, leaflets or posters to raise community awareness. How will it be organised? **Evaluation:** Are items re-used? Are the collections supported? Can the children give examples of re-use of materials?	System

'Ourselves' topic development sheet

Possible opportunities for design and technology activities:

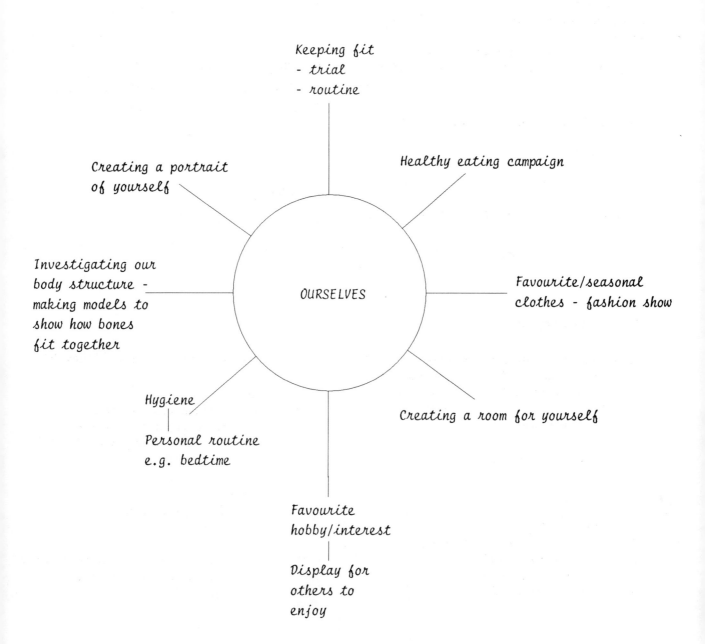

Keeping fit
- trial
- routine

Creating a portrait
of yourself

Healthy eating campaign

Investigating our
body structure -
making models to
show how bones
fit together

OURSELVES

Favourite/seasonal
clothes - fashion show

Hygiene

Personal routine
e.g. bedtime

Creating a room for yourself

Favourite
hobby/interest

Display for
others to
enjoy

'Ourselves' activity planning sheet 1

Theme/topic: *Ourselves*

Activity: *Who am I?*

Encourages individual activity; group/pair discussion

Setting the context (putting the children in the picture)

Talk about themselves, their interests, their friends etc.

Bring in photos of themselves, families, friends

Play games - Guess who? Look at special uniforms, equipment associated with interest

---

Particular resources, equipment

Photographs of people

Game - e.g. Guess who?

Books e.g. Who am I? (autobiographies, articles)

Possible contexts

Home	✔	Community	✔
School	✔	Business	
Recreation	✔	& industry	

Possible outcomes

Artefact	✔	*News-sheet, painting*
System		*collage*
Environment		

IT links

Word processing; graphics; DTP

Possible development:

Informing others about themselves
- *to help a new child settle in the class*
- *to help everyone to get to know each other at the start of the year, in a new school . . .*

'Brainstorm' – what could they do?

Make
- *a collage which portrays their personality and interests*
- *poster including personal details*
- *zig-zag booklet*

Write
- *a descriptive piece*

Create
- *a 'coat of arms', portraying their personality and interests*
- *a newsheet*

Evaluate
Did people make a correct guess? Did it portray the 'real' you? Was it eye-catching? What could be improved?

Plan, make, evaluate, modify...
What information do I want to pass on (personal appearance, likes, dislikes, interests, family members, friends . . .)?

'Ourselves' activity planning sheet 2

Theme/topic: *Ourselves*
Activity: *Healthy eating campaign*
Encourages group work

Setting the context (putting the children in the picture)

Visit local health clinic
Evaluating school dinners
Food - likes/dislikes   Video - healthy eating
School tuck shop   Visiting speaker: nurse
Visit health food shop

Particular resources, equipment

Posters; leaflets from clinic, supermarkets relating to food and healthy eating;
Magazines; non-fiction books relating to food

NB 'other cultures'

Games and rules

Possible contexts

Home	✔	Community	✔
School	✔	Business	
Recreation		& industry	

Possible outcomes

Artefact	✔	*e.g. game*
System	✔	*e.g. puppet play, campaign*
Environment	✔	*e.g. display in school*

IT links
Word processing; graphics; DTP

Database - information about eating habits

Possible development:

As part of science/health education project children evaluate materials from which they can gain information about healthy eating e.g. video, leaflet, poster, game
Are they easy to understand? Do the main points stand out? Are they attractive?.

What could the children do to help others realise the importance of healthy eating?

Evaluate
How well did they work together?
What might they improve?
What did they enjoy doing most?
How good was the campaign?
- questionnaire to other classes, home, dinner ladies,
Have eating habits changed?

'Brainstorm' ideas
- make a poster, leaflet
- make a display in school
- create a puppet play
- make a game

Decide who does what
What resources are needed?
What audience?
What timescale?

Plan, make, evaluate, modify

'Houses and homes' topic development sheet 1

Possible opportunities for design and technology activities:

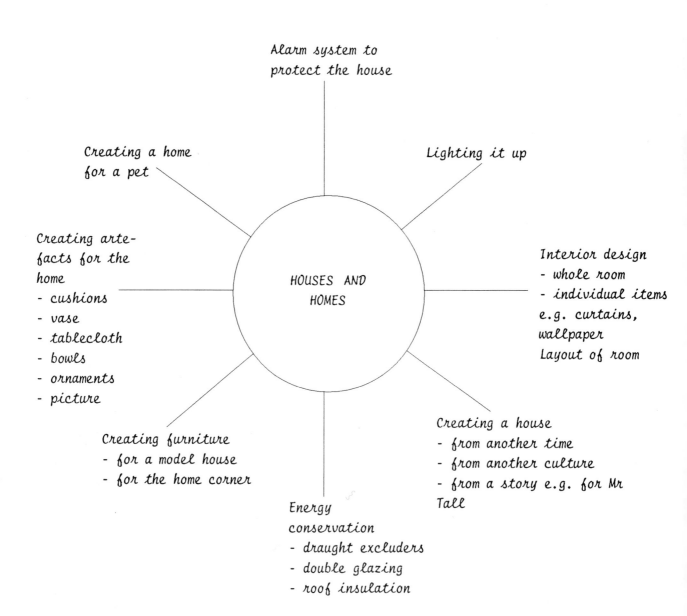

Alarm system to protect the house

Creating a home for a pet

Lighting it up

Creating arte-facts for the home
- cushions
- vase
- tablecloth
- bowls
- ornaments
- picture

HOUSES AND HOMES

Interior design
- whole room
- individual items e.g. curtains, wallpaper
Layout of room

Creating furniture
- for a model house
- for the home corner

Creating a house
- from another time
- from another culture
- from a story e.g. for Mr Tall

Energy conservation
- draught excluders
- double glazing
- roof insulation

'Houses and homes' activity planning sheet 1

Theme/topic: *Houses and homes*
Activity: *Laying the 'table'*
Encourages group or pair work

Setting the context (putting the children in the picture)

Discussion about different meals, celebrations from children's and other cultures and times

Possible contexts

Home	✔	Community	✔
School		Business	
Recreation		& industry	

Possible outcomes

Artefact   ✔
System
Environment ✔

Particular resources, equipment

Cutlery, paper plates

Magazines

IT links
Word processing; graphics

Possible development:

Identify need for laying the 'table' e.g. teddy bears' picnic
- type of people e.g. toys, adults, children
- type of meal e.g. tea, dinner, lunch picnic
- type of occasion e.g. birthday party, anniversary, arrival of new baby, wedding

Some points to consider:

colour scheme; number and type of plates and cutlery; napkins; table cloth; flowers; other decorations; seating; table shape; food

Evaluate
Do others want to sit at the table?
Is it colour co-ordinated?
Do people know where to sit?
Is it appropriate for the meal that is to be served?
Is it appropriate for the people who will sit at the table?

Plan, make/do, evaluate, modify

'Houses and homes' activity planning sheet 2

Theme/topic: Houses and homes
Activity: Alarm!
Encourages group work

Setting the context (putting the children in the picture)

Crime prevention - what can be done?
Visit of crime prevention officer
What alarms could be made?
Neighbourhood watch scheme.

Particular resources, equipment

Electrical equipment

Possible contexts

Home	✔	Community	✔
School	✔	Business	
Recreation		& industry	

Possible outcomes

Artefact		
System	✔	e.g. alarm system
Environment		

IT links
Control

Possible development:

Using existing home corner or model building, can the children devise an alarm system that will work every time someone steps on the front door mat?

Points to consider:
- type of alarm e.g. buzzer, light
- type of switch
- materials that could be used
- how it can be hidden

Evaluate
What difficulties were encountered?
Does the alarm work when the mat is stepped on?
Does it stop when the person gets off the mat?
Will the alarm attract attention?

Plan, make, evaluate, modify

'Toys and games' topic development sheet

Possible opportunities for design and technology activities:

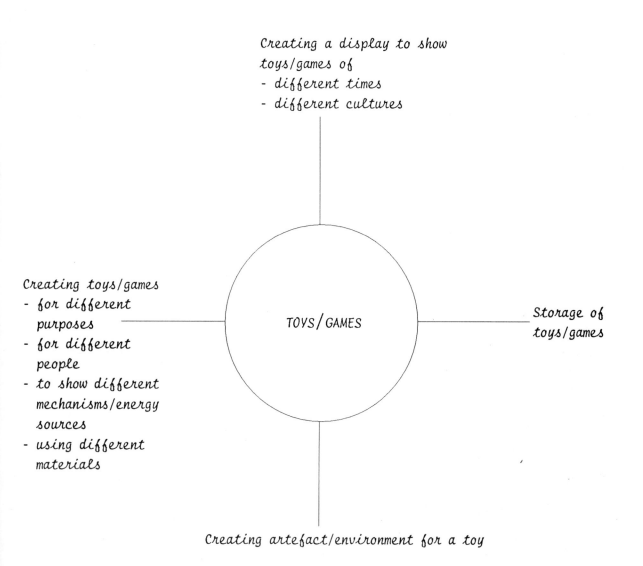

Creating a display to show
toys/games of
- different times
- different cultures

Creating toys/games
- for different
  purposes
- for different
  people
- to show different
  mechanisms/energy
  sources
- using different
  materials

TOYS/GAMES

Storage of
toys/games

Creating artefact/environment for a toy

'Toys and games' activity planning sheet 1

Theme/topic: *Toys / games*
Activity: *Making a game*
Encourages group or pair work

Setting the context (putting the children in the picture)

Looking at games
Games of other times, cultures
Playing diferent games.

Particular resources, equipment

Collection of games

Possible contexts

Home	✔	Community	✔
School	✔	Business	
Recreation	✔	& industry	

Possible outcomes

Artefact ✔
System
Environment

IT links

Word processing, graphics, DTP

Possible development:

The children are bored at wet playtime. What game could they make to play with their friends?

Evaluate a selection of games in the classroom. What do they enjoy playing? Why?

Evaluate
Play the game.
Does it work? Is it fun? Do others want to play? Are they still bored when it's wet at playtime? Could other classes use the game?

What will they make?
- a board game
- a quiz game
Who will they work with?
What materials will be needed?
Think about design

Plan, make, evaluate, modify

'Toys and games' activity planning sheet 2

Theme/topic: *Toys/games*
Activity: *Making a toy*
Encourages working in groups, pairs or individually

Setting the context (putting the children in the picture)

Looking at a variety of toys from different times and cultures, for children with a disability, for younger children, for babies. What is the purpose of the toy? History of toys.

Particular resources, equipment

Collection of toys with different mechanisms. Rubber bands; wood; glue gun; variety of materials; construction kits; variety of boxes; containers

---

Possible contexts

Home	✔	Community	✔
School	✔	Business	
Recreation	✔	& Industry	✔

Possible outcomes

Artefact	✔	*toy*
System		
Environment		

IT links

Graphics
Control

Possible development:

Evaluate collection of toys.
What do children like about them?
What different mechanisms can they find?
What materials have been used?

Make a toy
What is the need for the toy - younger brother/sister, for a baby, for themselves, for a disabled child?
Considerations might include: materials to be used; mechanism if any, size, shape, colour

Evaluate
Does their toy 'work' Do they like it? What could they do better next time? What difficulties did they experience during the making of the toy?

Plan, make, evaluate, modify

'Books' topic development sheet

Possible opportunities for design and technology activities:

Creation of puppets
to help tell a story

Creation of an
illustration
to 'liven up'
a dull book

Borrowing
system for books

Creation of a taped
story for a younger
audience

Book arrangement in
corridor, classroom . . .

BOOKS,   STORIES,
POEMS,   RHYMES

Attractive library,
reading corner

Creation of a story to
read to the nursery
children on an impend-
ing visit

Creation of
- own books
- books for different audiences
  - covers

Exploring stories, poems,
rhymes from different
cultures. Opportunities exist
in almost any book for design
and technology activities e.g.
Hansel and Gretel - what could they
have used for a trail?
Anansi - How could Anansi get the
breadfruit from the tree?

'Books' activity planning sheet 1

Theme/topic: Books - stories, poems, rhymes
Activity: Making a book cover
Encourages group, pair or individual work

Setting the context (putting the children in the picture)

Evaluating book cover; inviting a graphic artist into school; asking at the library about the cover people like.
Does the cover encourage people to borrow books?
What do people like about different covers?

Possible contexts

Home	✔	Community	✔
School	✔	Business	
Recreation	✔	& industry	✔

Possible outcomes

Artefact	✔	book cover
System		
Environment		

Particular resources, equipment

Variety of book covers
Graphic materials
Stencils

IT links

Word processing, graphics, database - information about book covers

---

Possible development:

Many of the books look unattractive in the book corner. Their covers are ripped and torn. Could the children make some new ones?

Some points to consider:
material for cover - test for e.g. durability; print size; type of illustrations

Evaluate
Does the book corner look more attractive?
Do the covers look better?
Do the children want to borrow more books?
Do the children borrow books that were previously not borrowed?

Plan, make, evaluate, modify
Covers could be costed. Could standard size covers be made and sold?

'Books' activity planning sheet 2

Theme/topic: *Books - stories, poems, rhymes*
Activity: *Creating a book corner*
Encourages group work

Setting the context (putting the children in the picture)

Visiting the library
Visiting the school library; visiting book corners in other classes

---

Possible contexts

Home	✔	Community	✔
School	✔	Business	
Recreation	✔	& industry	✔

Particular resources, equipment

Textiles, filling material

Possible outcomes

Artefact	✔
System	
Environment	✔

IT links

Word processing, graphics, DTP

Possible development:

Class book corner is not used very much. What could be done to increase its use?

Brainstorm
- *rearrange books*
- *paint bookcases*
- *keep tidy*
- *put home-made books in it*
- *move its position*
- *make cushions*
- *advertise 'favourite books'*
- *allow it to be used at playtime*

Evaluate
Do more children use it? How can we be sure (survey)? Does it look attractive? Are books easily accessible? What else could be done to increase its use?

Plan, make/do, evaluate, modify

'Movement' topic development sheet

Possible opportunities for design and technology activities:

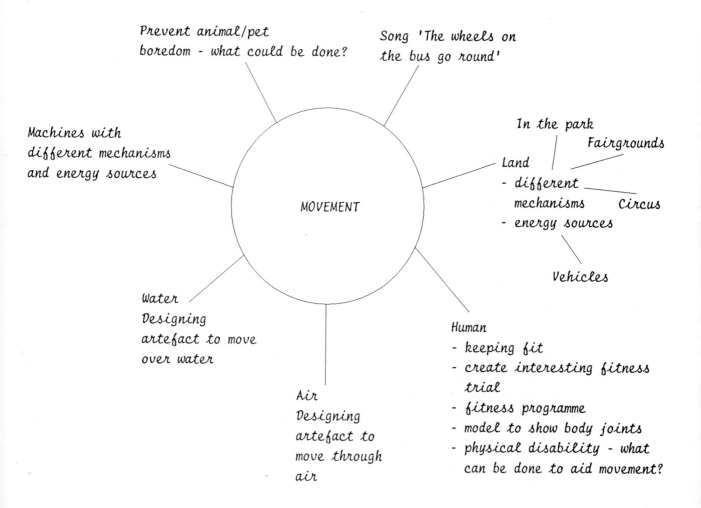

Prevent animal/pet boredom - what could be done?

Song 'The wheels on the bus go round'

Machines with different mechanisms and energy sources

In the park

Fairgrounds

Land
- different mechanisms
- energy sources

Circus

Vehicles

MOVEMENT

Water
Designing artefact to move over water

Air
Designing artefact to move through air

Human
- keeping fit
- create interesting fitness trial
- fitness programme
- model to show body joints
- physical disability - what can be done to aid movement?

'Movement' activity planning sheet 1

Theme/topic: *Movement*
Activity: *A 'pick-up'*
Encourages group, pair work

Setting the context (putting the children in the picture)

Picking things up.
Body movements; how far can we stretch?
Look at mechanisms that open and shut.

Possible contexts

Home	✔	Community	✔
School	✔	Business	
Recreation		& industry	

Possible outcomes

Artefact ✔
System
Environment

Particular resources, equipment

Items on the market e.g. tongs, long-handled objects, squeezy mop (to show mechanisms)

IT links

Control

Possible development:

There are huge piles of chip papers outside the school. The caretaker has a bad back. What could we make/do so that it is easier for him/her to pick them up? (Could be modelled with construction kit)

Look at existing equipment
What could be made?

- *sharp ended, long-handled stick*
- *long-handled tongs*
- *long-handled brush/pan*
- *motorised vehicle (model)*

What materials would be appropriate?

Evaluate
Does the 'picker-up' pick up?
Does it do the job easily?
Is it strong?
Does the caretaker have to bend down to use it?

Plan, make, evaluate, modify

'Movement' activity planning sheet 2

Theme/topic: *Movement*
Activity: *Creating a vehicle*

Setting the context (putting the children in the picture)

Discussion about different vehicles
What do they all have (wheels)?
Vehicles for different purposes

Possible contexts

Home		Community	✔
School	✔	Business	
Recreation	✔	& industry	

Possible outcomes

Artefact ✔
System
Environment

Particular resources, equipment

Different shaped boxes, glue gun, wood, wheels, dowel

IT links

Control

Possible development:

Make a vehicle with wheels that move (or just with wheels if that is more appropriate) Identify the need for it. What will it be for? Carry passengers, goods, fantasy vehicle. Think about e.g. size, shape, materials, wheel fixing

Plan, make, evaluate, modify

Do the wheels move?
Does the vehicle serve the purpose for which it was intended?
What improvement could be made?
Are the wheels firmly fixed?
Will the vehicle move over different surfaces?

'Out and about' topic development sheet

Possible opportunities for design and technology activities:

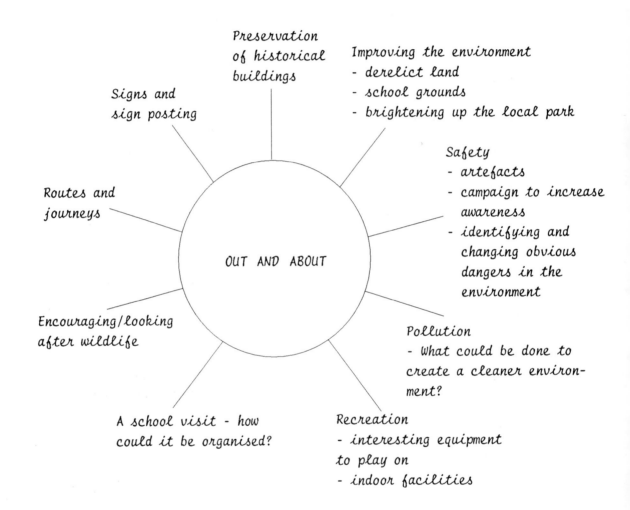

'Out and about' activity planning sheet 1

Theme/topic: *Out and about*
Activity: *Improving the local environment - around the school, derelict piece of land Encourages group work*

Setting the context (putting the children in the picture)

Research re pollution
Walk around site to be improved
Ask others about way land could be improved
Ask local council for information

Possible contexts

Home		Community	✔
School	✔	Business	
Recreation	✔	& industry	✔

Possible outcomes

Artefact
System
Environment ✔

Particular resources, equipment

Video/TV programme on pollution, derelict land, litter . . .

IT links

Word processing, graphics, DTP
Database - information on improvements

Possible development:

Identify area to be improved; discuss possible improvements; take account of others' ideas. Use a questionnaire to survey local residents, ideas if appropriate

Ideas might include:
planting seeds, bulbs; new litter bins; clean and restock school pond; provide seating, playground games; build a new leisure centre; environmental area; shopping arcade, play area
(some of these will involve modelling solutions)

Evaluate
How well did they work together? What difficulties did they encounter? Were the needs of the disabled taken into account? What do others think of the improvements?

Plan, make, or carry out action plan, evaluate, modify
Costing solutions will be appropriate in some cases

'Out and about' activity planning sheet 2

Theme/topic: *Out and about*
Activity: *Be seen!*
Encourages group work/individual work

Setting the context (putting the children in the picture)

Information from ROSPA about accidents in the dark; recommendations to avoid an accident; talk about existing artefacts that can be used; what can we see in the dark? What does 'luminous' mean?

Possible contexts

Home	✔	Community	✔
School	✔	Business	
Recreation	✔	& industry	✔

Possible outcomes

Artefact ✔ *e.g. sticker, armband*
System
Environment

Particular resources, equipment

Variety of existing artefacts, used at night.
Luminous fabrics, card, paint, paper

IT links

Word processing, graphics, database - information gathered about existing products

---

Possible development:

As the dark evenings approach, motorists find it more difficult to see pedestrians. What could the children do to make sure they are clearly visible? Evaluate existing artefacts. Test to see if they make the children more visible. What kind of artefacts do the children prefer?
- an item of clothing
- a sticker
- an armband . . .
What kind of material could they use?
What colour could they use? Carry out any necessary tests

Design, plan, make, evaluate, modify

The item could be costed, mass produced and sold, if appropriate

Could they be seen more clearly?
Do they like the finished artefact?
Is it easy to wear?
Do others like the finished artefact?
Do they want to buy it?

'Celebrations and festivals' topic development sheet

Possible opportunities for design and technology activities:

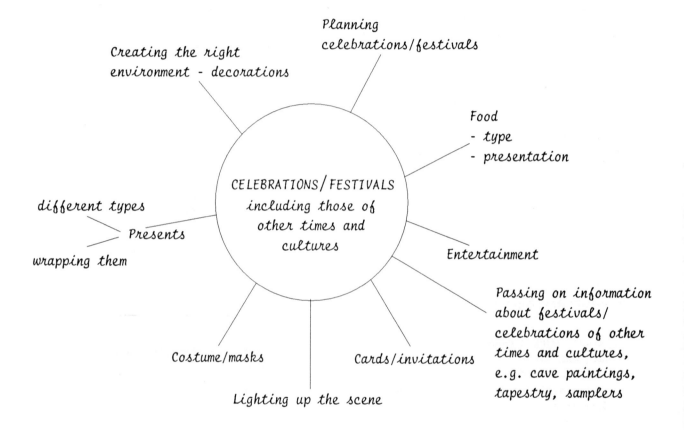

'Celebrations and festivals' activity planning sheet 1

Theme/topic: *Celebrations/festivals*
Activity: *Making a card*
Encourages individual activity; group/pair discussion

Setting the context (putting the children in the picture)

Discussion of why cards are sent
Cards of others times and cultures
Cost of cards
Cards using recycled paper

Possible contexts

Home	✔	Community	✔
School	✔	Business	
Recreation	✔	& industry	✔

Possible outcomes

Artefact ✔
System ✔
Environment

Particular resources, equipment

Variety of cards for different purposes
Variety of fabrics, sewing equipment
Background knowledge of simple mechanisms

IT links

Word processing, graphics

Possible development:

Evaluation of a card collection could include:
- different audiences
- different purposes
- use of colour, print size
- type of message
- type of illustration
- use of moveable parts
- use of sound, smell, tactile surfaces

Need for a card could include; birthday, Christmas, Valentines day, new baby, retirement, new home, congratulations, Diwali

What should be included? Think about colour, size, message, moveable part, illustration. Extension - cost card and sell at school. How will the production line operate?

What problems were encountered during making? How were they overcome? Did the person like the card? Did they sell well? How much profit?

Plan, make, evaluate, modify

'Celebrations and festivals' activity planning sheet 2

Theme/topic: *Celebrations/festivals*
Activity: *Planning a party*
Encourages group work

Setting the context (putting the children in the picture)

Discussion about parties they have liked/disliked
Reasons for parties
Parties of other times and cultures

Possible contexts

Home	✔	Community	✔
School	✔	Business	
Recreation	✔	& industry	✔

Possible outcomes

Artefact	✔	*invitation, place mats*
System	✔	*main outcome*
Environment	✔	*decorated venue*

Particular resources, equipment

Cookery ingredients and equipment
Puppets
Old cards
Invitations

IT links

Word processing, graphics, database e.g. food likes/dislikes

Possible development:

Opportunities for a party could include: school birthday; entertaining playgroup or over 60s club; Christmas party; Diwali; end of year party

Brainstorm
What should be included?
Games, food, decorations, puppet play, concert, invitations, place mats, date, time, place

What is possible, what is not.
Who does what?
Timescale for each part

Evaluate
What problems/successes for each group? Was it put together successfully? Did everyone enjoy it? How did the children know – asking visitors, atmosphere, listening to visitors' comments, receiving letters of thanks . .
.

Plan, make, evaluate, modify

'Shops and shopping' topic development sheet

Possible opportunities for design and technology activities:

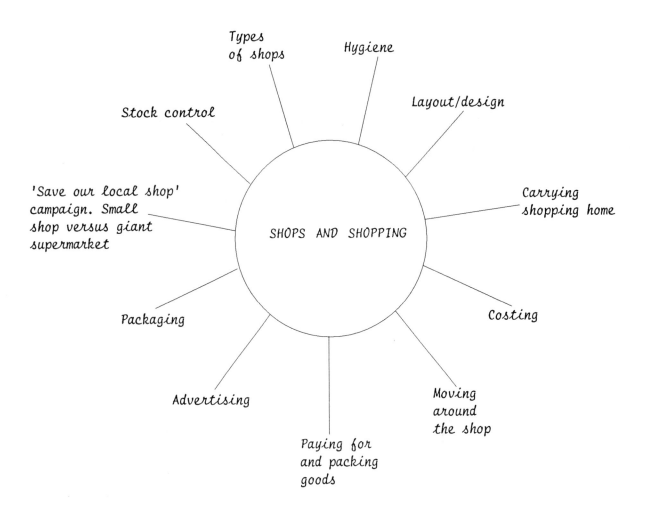

'Shops and shopping' activity planning sheet 1

Theme/topic: *Shops and shopping*
Activity: *Creating 'Our shop'*
Encourages group work

Setting the context (putting the children in the picture)

Visit variety of shops
Talk from shopkeeper
Video
Pictures/books about shops

Possible contexts

Home	Community ✔
School ✔	Business
Recreation	& industry ✔

Possible outcomes

Artefact	✔	*e.g. products in shop*
System	✔	*e.g. buying and selling*
Environment	✔	*e.g. shop*

Particular resources, equipment

Shopping bags, goods for shop

IT links

Word processing, graphics, DTP, spreadsheet eg products people buy
Database e.g. products liked/disliked

Possible development:

'Our shop' could be imaginary or real. Create a shop in school.
What type of shop? How will it be stocked. Will goods be ready-made, made by pupils, environmentally friendly? How will layout be organised? Who will price goods? Where will customers pay? What currency? How will the goods be packed (environmentally friendly bags, boxes, shopping bags)? How will a record of stock be kept? How will goods be advertised? Will there be 'special lines'? Who will do what (making, displaying, selling, wrapping, advertising)?

Plan, make/do, evaluate, modify

Evaluate
Do people use the shop? Are the shelves well stocked? Does it look attractive? What items sell best? Can customers reach the shelves, items for sale?

'Shops and shopping' activity planning sheet 2

Theme/topic: *Shops and shopping*
Activity: *An attractive package*
Encourages pair work/individual work

Setting the context (putting the children in the picture)

Discussion about packaging; packaging they like; Risk of litter
Reasons for different types of packaging

Possible contexts

Home	✔	Community	✔
School	✔	Business	
Recreation		& industry	✔

Possible outcomes

Artefact ✔ *e.g. attractive package*
System
Environment

Particular resources, equipment

Range of packaging to show different designs, materials, size, printing

---

IT links

Word processing, graphics

Possible development:

A collection of loose sweets needs a container (the dog chewed the original one). Could the children make a packet for the sweets?

What type of material would be best? Points to consider might include strength, crushability, colour, size. Is it attractive, waterproof . . . ?

Plan, make/do, evaluate, modify

How much would the packet cost to make? Would bulk orders reduce the price?

Evaluate
Do the sweets fit in?
Is the packet attractive?
Do others like it? Is it strong?
Could the dog chew this packet?

'Transport' topic development sheet

Possible opportunities for design and technology activities:

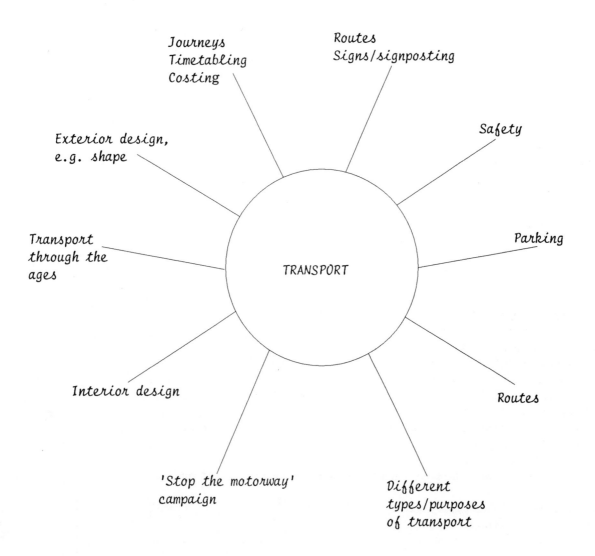

Journeys
Timetabling
Costing

Routes
Signs/signposting

Safety

Exterior design,
e.g. shape

Parking

Transport
through the
ages

TRANSPORT

Interior design

Routes

'Stop the motorway'
campaign

Different
types/purposes
of transport

'Transport' activity planning sheet 1

Theme/topic: *Transport*
Activity: *Directing the traffic*
Encourages group work (individuals could work on own arrangement)

Setting the context (putting the children in the picture)

Looking at existing signs in the environment e.g. road, rail, canal, river, airport. What are they used for - directing transport, information?
What shape, colour, size?
Why are they in particular positions?

Particular resources, equipment

ROSPA materials; replica signs from e.g. toyset, road safety officer

---

Possible contexts

Home	Community ✔
School ✔	Business
Recreation	& industry

Possible outcomes

Artefact	✔	*e.g. new signs*
System	✔	*e.g. road system on a*
Environment		*play board*

IT links

Word processing; DTP
Graphics
Control

Possible development:

Using - playboard
*   - playground*
*   - large scale map as a base board*
Traffic needs directing otherwise accidents, congestion occur. How can the traffic be directed safely?
What might be needed (signs, road markings, newssheet to tell local people of any changes)?
Where are the major junctions?
Are there any railway crossings? What information should be put on the signs?
Are the existing ones appropriate?
Where should the signs be put?

Plan, make/do, evaluate, modify

Evaluate
Does the traffic run smoothly?
Does the railway crossing barrier light at the right time?
Can the signs be seen?
Do they block the vision of the car driver?
Do people know of the changes?

'Transport' activity planning sheet 2

Theme/topic: *Transport*
Activity: *A more sociable ride!*
Encourages group work

Setting the context (putting the children in the picture)

Bus ride;
role play in the class;
coach journey;
discussion about journeys they have made;
guest speaker from bus/coach firm

Particular resources, equipment

Possible contexts

Home	Community ✔
School	Business
Recreation ✔	& industry ✔

Possible outcomes

Artefact	✔	*e.g. model of interior*
System	✔	*e.g. getting in & out of seats*
Environment	✔	*e.g. interior of bus*

IT links

Graphics

Possible development:

Ride on the bus or coach may cause problems - friends cannot sit together, children cannot talk easily to each other unless they stand up. What could be done?
Look at seating arrangement
Try different arrangements (use real chairs, wood blocks, paper on a scale base board).
What considerations?
Easy access to all seats, number of seats (economic considerations) safety, access for disabled;
Research into existing seating arrangements in e.g. tourist, luxury, football coaches

Evaluate
Is it more sociable?
Do others like the new arrangement?
Do other factors make the original design better?
Does the purpose for which the bus/coach is used determine the seating arrangement?

Plan, make/do, evaluate, modify
interior arrangments
Could model, use real furniture, make scale drawings

'Holidays and leisure' topic development sheet

Possible opportunities for design and technology activities:

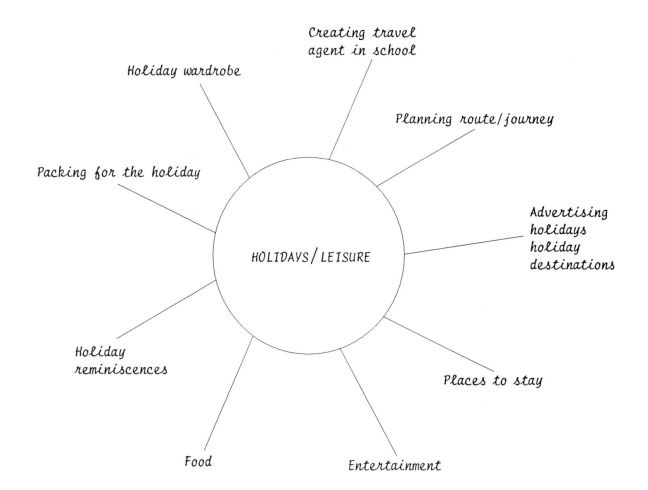

'Holidays and leisure' activity planning sheet 1

Theme/topic: *Holidays and leisure*
Activity: *Packing the case*
Encourages working in groups, pairs, individually

Setting the context (putting the children in the picture)

Going on holiday
What similarities/differences between home and being away?
What activities?
What weather?

Possible contexts

Home	✔	Community	✔
School	✔	Business	
Recreation	✔	& industry	

Particular resources, equipment

Different cases

Possible outcomes

Artefact
System ✔
Environment

IT links

Possible development:

Packing a case; what will need to be done? Choose clothes, shoes, games, books, etc.
Wash, iron clothes; put in washing things.
In what order will jobs need to be done?
In what order will things be packed - e.g. dirty shoes in middle of case, washing things at bottom?

Plan, do, evaluate, modify
Would a flowchart help?

Evaluate
Did the children have all they needed? Was it all in good condition when it arrived at its destination? Did it all fit in the case? Was the case too heavy to carry?

'Holidays and leisure' activity planning sheet 2

Theme/topic: Holidays/leisure
Activity: A holiday brochure
Encourages group, pair or individual work

Setting the context (putting the children in the picture)

Going on holiday - what do we do?
What do we need? Why do we have a holiday?
What places have the children visited?

Possible contexts

Home	✔	Community	✔
School	✔	Business	
Recreation	✔	& industry	✔

Particular resources, equipment

Holiday brochures
Newspaper cuttings
Magazines

Possible outcomes

Artefact   ✔   e.g. brochure
System
Environment

IT links

Word processing, graphics. DTP,
Database - holiday bookings from another class

Possible development:

What could the children make to advertise a holiday?
Poster, brochure, booklet
Considerations might include: size, colour, type of writing,
layout, graphics material to be used, pictures, information
to be given

**Plan, make/do,
evaluate, modify**

Evaluate
What difficulties were experienced
in the making?
What improvements?
Is the information readily avail-
able?
Does the brochure look attractive?
Can it be read easily?
If another class is involved which
holiday would they choose? Why?

PRACTICAL SKILLS AND TECHNIQUES

Working in paper and wood 1 – Scoring/Folding

Scoring

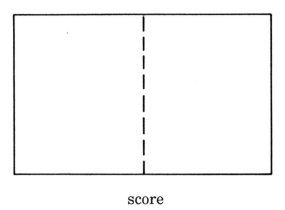

score

Place ruler along line to be scored.
Run a knife (not very sharp) or scissors along ruler.
Don't press too hard or you will cut the paper or card

Folding
(without scoring)

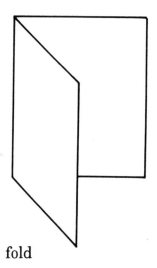

fold

Get the children to line up the two edges and ensure that they are straight before pressing down with a finger along the fold line. This will help to prevent several fold marks on the paper or card.

PRACTICAL SKILLS AND TECHNIQUES

Working in paper and wood 2 – Joining (a)

(i) Slots

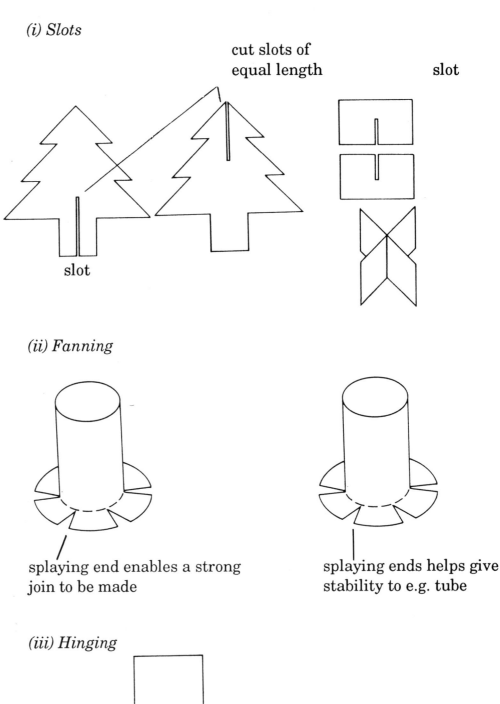

cut slots of
equal length

slot

slot

(ii) Fanning

splaying end enables a strong
join to be made

splaying ends helps give
stability to e.g. tube

(iii) Hinging

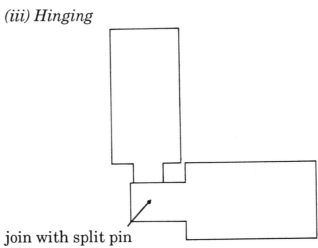

join with split pin

Working in paper and wood 2 – Joining (b)

(iv) Saddle joint

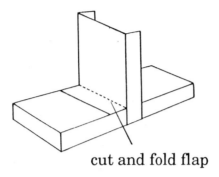

cut and fold flap

(v) Sockets

Sockets can be made from card or paper, to hold card, paper or wood

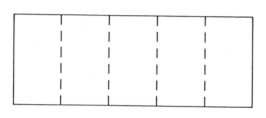 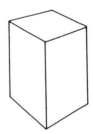

i) score card and fold and glue

ii) measurement dependent on thickness of material to fit into socket

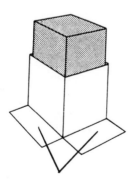

iii) push post into socket

score card/paper and fold back flaps

Working in paper and wood 2 – Joining (c)

(vi) Joining two pieces of wood

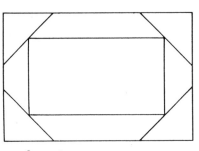

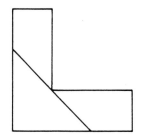

stick card triangle on to wood

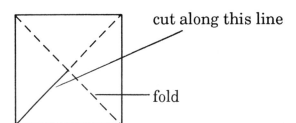

a chassis

(vii) Joining three pieces of wood

card square

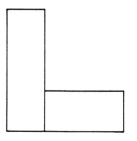

cut along this line

fold

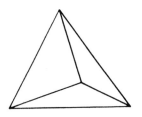

fold card

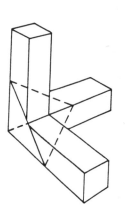

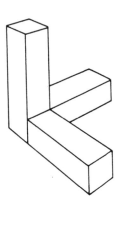

PRACTICAL SKILLS AND TECHNIQUES

Working in paper and wood 3 – Cutting

a) Scissors
(are left handed scissors available?)

b) Craft knife
(check LEA policy before use)

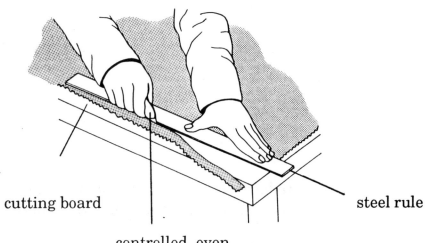

cutting board   steel rule

controlled, even
pressure for each cut

c) Hacksaw

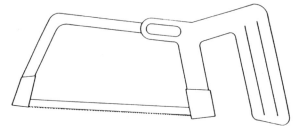

Move slowly backwards and forwards. Do not press down

Keep wood secure on a bench hook

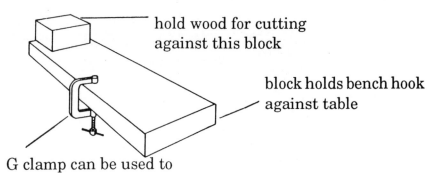

hold wood for cutting
against this block

block holds bench hook
against table

G clamp can be used to
secure bench hook to table

PRACTICAL SKILLS AND TECHNIQUES

Working in paper and wood 4 – Drilling and making holes

Drilling

Ensure children are not drilling through the wood onto a table. Put in a protective layer. Drill stands can be used to keep drill secure.

Making holes

Bradawls

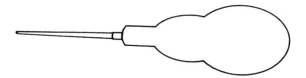

Bradawls are very useful for this. (Soldering irons can be used on plastics but this can damage the soldering iron)

Hole punchers

It is useful to have different types available. Single hole punchers are useful especially if the hole size can be adjusted, though they can be difficult to use for those with a small hand span.

PRACTICAL SKILLS AND TECHNIQUES

Mechanisms 1 – Wheels

a) Rotation on card

(i)

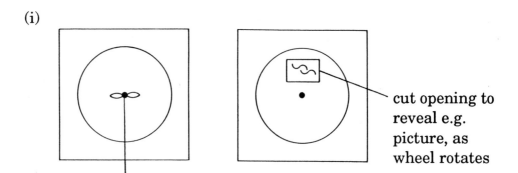

brass paper fastener

(ii)

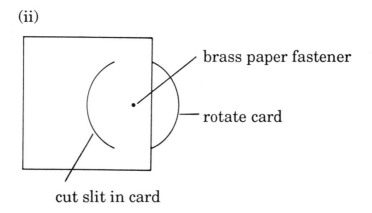

b) Rotation on chassis

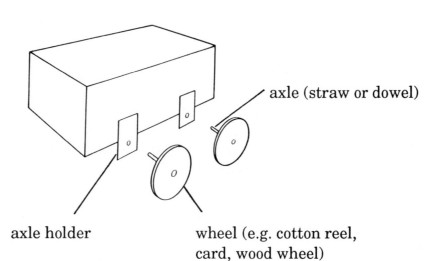

Mechanisms 2 – Slide/Spring/Locks

Slide

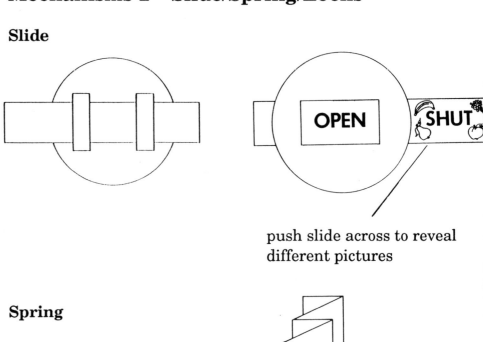

push slide across to reveal
different pictures

Spring

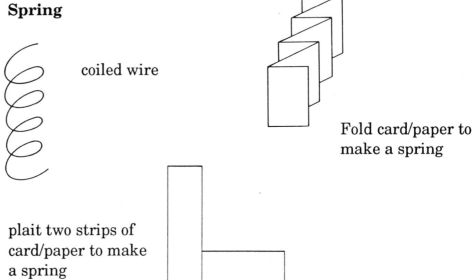

coiled wire

Fold card/paper to
make a spring

plait two strips of
card/paper to make
a spring

Locks

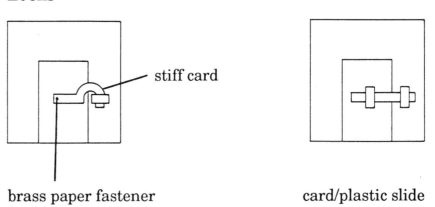

stiff card

brass paper fastener

card/plastic slide

Mechanisms 3 – Gears/Pulleys

Gears
It may be better for children to use construction kits as it is difficult to make gears that mesh properly.

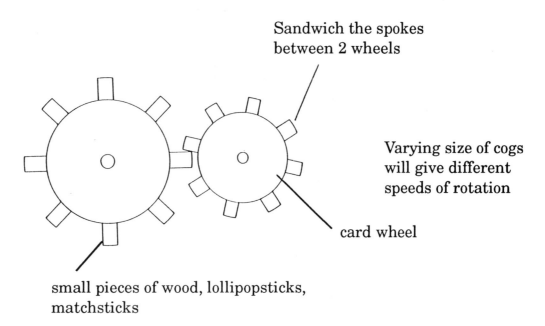

Sandwich the spokes between 2 wheels

Varying size of cogs will give different speeds of rotation

card wheel

small pieces of wood, lollipopsticks, matchsticks

Pulley

Pulley wheels are wheels with a groove.
Two pulleys halve the effort required to lift a load

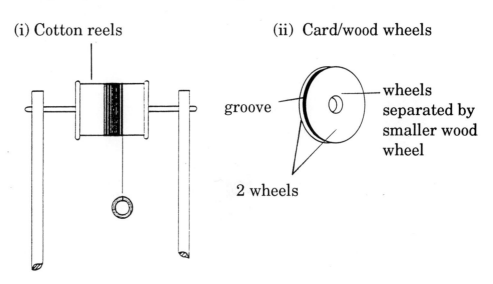

(i) Cotton reels

(ii) Card/wood wheels

groove

wheels separated by smaller wood wheel

2 wheels

Mechanisms 4 – Lever/Cam and crank

Lever

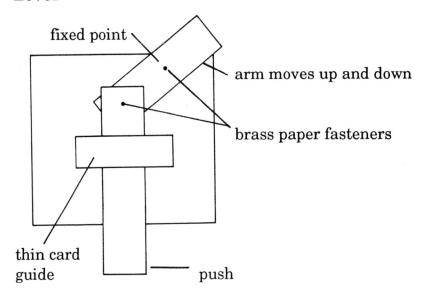

fixed point

arm moves up and down

brass paper fasteners

thin card guide

push

Cam and crank

Cam

They change rotary movement to up and down movement

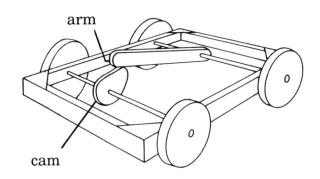

arm

cam

as wheels go round cam goes up and down and moves arm up and down

Crank

crank

Mechanisms 5 – Simple handles/Hinges
Simple handles

art straw bent into shape

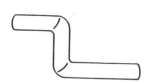

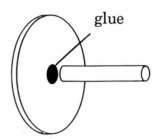

glue

dowel or straw pushed into hole in a card/wood circle. Glue may give a firmer fix.

Hinges

i) cut out window. Use e.g. masking tape as hinges

ii) cut on solid lines

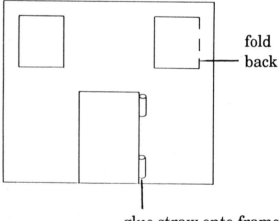

fold back

glue straw onto frame

iii)
cut out door

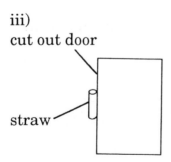

straw

use thin piece of dowel or smaller straw to fix door into frame

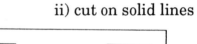

PRACTICAL SKILLS AND TECHNIQUES

Energy 1 – Pneumatics and hydraulics/ Rubber band

Pneumatics/hydraulics

lifting action

Pneumatics – when the air is forced along the tube and pushes the plunger up at the other end

Hydraulics – when water is the force

adding a little food colouring to the water helps the children to see what is happening

Different sized syringes 5ml or 10ml give different movement.

Air can be compressed and therefore it may be better to use hydraulics to lift a bigger/heavier weight.

tubing fits into syringe

simple pneumatics

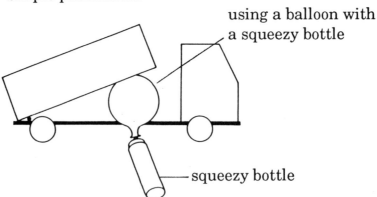

using a balloon with a squeezy bottle

squeezy bottle

Rubber band

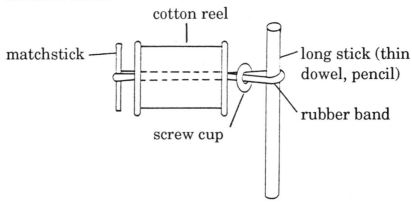

cotton reel

matchstick

long stick (thin dowel, pencil)

rubber band

screw cup

Energy 2 – Water and wind power/ Electricity

Water/wind power

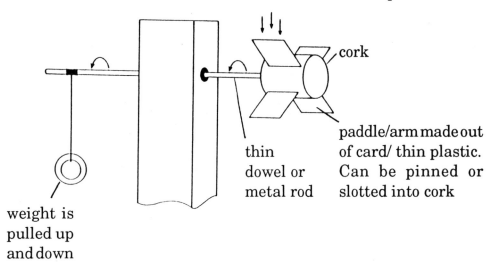

water or wind to turn paddle

cork

paddle/arm made out of card/ thin plastic. Can be pinned or slotted into cork

thin dowel or metal rod

weight is pulled up and down

Electricity

battery & holder

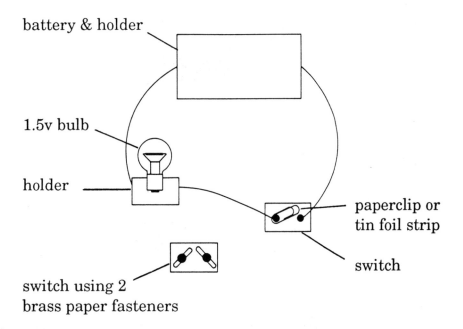

1.5v bulb

holder

paperclip or tin foil strip

switch

switch using 2 brass paper fasteners

N.B. match battery power with bulbs
e.g. 1.5v battery 1.5v bulb ✔
3v battery 1.5v bulb ✗

motor or buzzer could replace bulb

Food

Simple techniques should be taught and used. These could include:

whisking	beating
mixing	stirring
rubbing (pastry)	creaming
spreading	separating (eggs)
scraping	coring
peeling	cutting
grating	

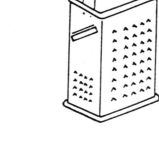

straining

rolling out (pastry)

Simple techniques associated with presentation are important e.g. cutting tomatoes, radishes into shapes; making open sandwiches look attractive by using colours and shapes effectively, garnishing, etc.

Textiles

Simple techniques should be taught and used. These could include:

threading a needle

flattened end
of thread

starting & finishing a thread
embroidery – stitches might include running, cross, chain, feather
stitches
button holes
printing on fabric using – paints
– crayons
patchwork
knitting - plain, pearl stitch
weaving (paper, wool)
tie dye
batch
appliqué
pom-pom
card wrapping

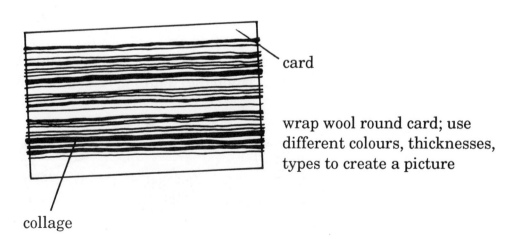

card

wrap wool round card; use
different colours, thicknesses,
types to create a picture

collage

PRACTICAL SKILLS AND TECHNIQUES

Art

Simple techniques should be taught and used. These could include:

colouring   lettering

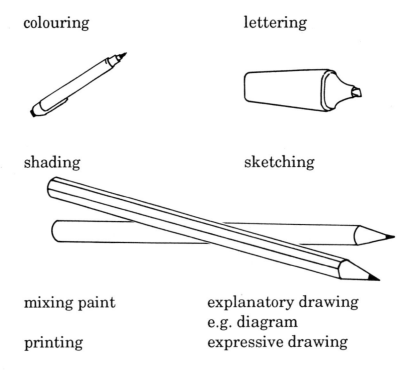

shading   sketching

mixing paint   explanatory drawing
                          e.g. diagram
printing   expressive drawing

Children should have experience of – working with chalks, char-coals, pastels, wax crayons, lead pencils, felt-tip pens, inks, paints

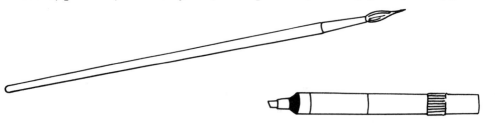

– collage work using a variety of materials. Using paper may involve: tearing, crumpling, quilling, folding

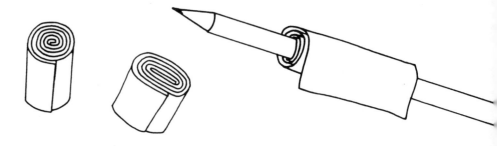

– using clay – may involve: making a hollow form, joining, slabbing and creating different surfaces and textures.

PRACTICAL SKILLS AND TECHNIQUES

Photography/Video

Photography

a) Pin-hole camera

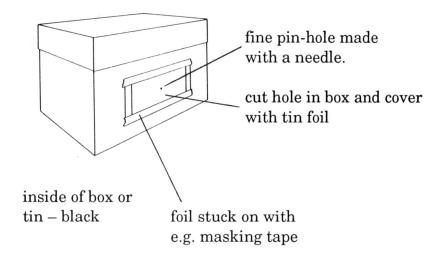

fine pin-hole made
with a needle.

cut hole in box and cover
with tin foil

inside of box or
tin – black

foil stuck on with
e.g. masking tape

b) Ordinary camera
Techniques could include:
– focusing
– holding camera properly (still, no fingers over lenses!)
– choosing film for effect (black and white or colour)

Video
Techniques could include:
– focusing
– zooming in and out
– panning
– creating a storyboard to indicate visual progression

9
Organisation and management

Classroom organisation and management

It will come as no great surprise to teachers that, as in all other areas of the curriculum, the successful implementation of design and technology relies to a great extent on the way in which the classroom is organised and managed. Although there is no one 'right way', there are certain issues that need to be considered both individually and in relation to one another.

The working space
Whether the activities are to take place in a classroom or a specialist room, the layout should be assessed.

– What kinds of activities will take place?
– How might this affect the type, amount and position of:
   • the furniture and storage space;
   • display space;
   • places to store unfinished work (models, paintings, sketches, folders)?

Bearing in mind these considerations, Figure 9.1 illustrates one example of a suitable layout for a working space.

Resources

Equipment and materials

– Easily accessible, clearly labelled and well stocked equipment and materials will encourage the children to make choices and to work independently.
– Different types of 'free' containers can be collected and used. These might include lidded, plastic film containers for glue; mushroom trays for such items as lollipop sticks, matchsticks and wool; sanded and varnished stacking vegetable trays for such items as paper and card; shoeboxes for electrical equipment.
– Readily available cleaning materials (including dustpan and brush, cloths for the floor and the tables, soap for hands and washing up, surface cleanser, towel, drying-up towel and plastic

Fig. 9.1 Suggested workspace layout

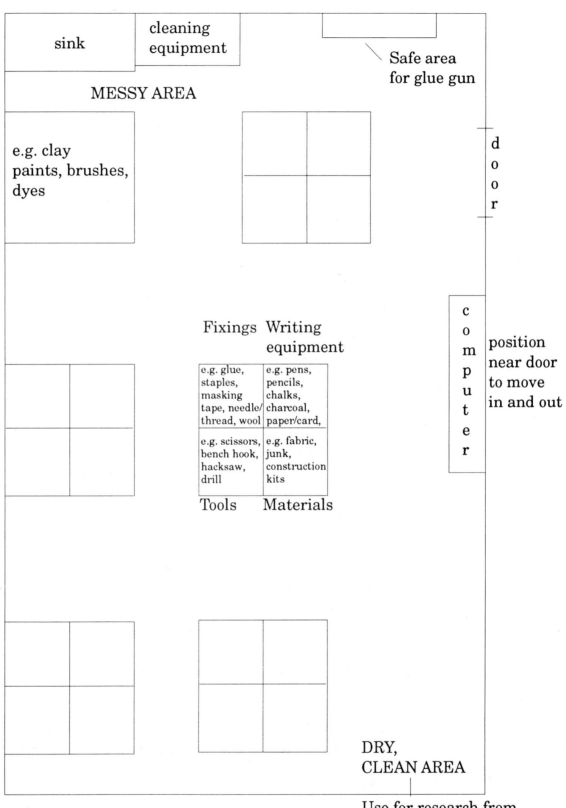

sink

cleaning equipment

Safe area for glue gun

MESSY AREA

e.g. clay paints, brushes, dyes

d o o r

Fixings | Writing equipment

| e.g. glue, staples, masking tape, needle/ thread, wool | e.g. pens, pencils, chalks, charcoal, paper/card, |
| e.g. scissors, bench hook, hacksaw, drill | e.g. fabric, junk, construction kits |

Tools   Materials

c o m p u t e r

position near door to move in and out

DRY, CLEAN AREA

Tables grouped:
enourages group work
large surface to work on
different activities at different tables

Use for research from reference books, gathering information from e.g. questionnaire, quiet discussion, interviewing visitors.

gloves) to encourage the children to clean and tidy up as they work. (Note: care should be taken to use only 'safe' cleansers.)
- Protective clothing (such as plastic aprons or old shirts) should be kept clean and hung where they can be reached easily by the children.
- Items that could be dangerous (such as glue guns and saws), or could need extra care (such as the computer), should be placed in a 'safe' area and children made aware of any special rules for their use.

Construction kits

Children find it very frustrating to discover that the vital piece needed to complete a model is missing. To reduce the chances of this happening, the children can be encouraged to:

- check all surfaces for 'odd' pieces when packing kits away;
- put pieces that 'turn up' at odd times into a special container, to be put away later.

Activities

Although the organisation of activities will obviously vary considerably according to the nature of the task in hand, some general considerations can be identified.

The introduction – setting the context

- Will the initial stimulus involve a visit, a visitor, a video, a slide presentation or a film? How will this be organised?

The activities themselves

- Will the activity be introduced, e.g. with a group or with the whole class?
- How will the children work, e.g. as individuals, in pairs or in small groups?
- Has sufficient time been allocated, e.g. for research, collecting information, planning and making, evaluation and any necessary redesigning?
- Will all the children be involved in design and technology or will some be involved in activities related to other curriculum areas?

The activities organisation sheet on p.xx illustrates various methods that can be adopted.

Children's recording of the activities

In addition to the final outcome, the children could be encouraged to record their on-going thoughts, ideas and modifications on paper. This may help them to view and plan the activity as a whole process.

Recording could be in:

- a loose-leaf folder;
- a zig-zag book;
- a booklet for each activity;
- a book kept specifically for all their design and technology activities.

Recordings could include:

- brainstorming ideas of group/class;
- group membership;
- allotted tasks for each group member;
- resources that are needed;
- designs;
- time allocation for each task;
- modifications that were needed/made;
- evaluations of any relevant existing artefacts, systems and environments;
- evaluation of own/group outcome.

Such recordings should not only help to clarify the children's thoughts concerning the activity, but should also provide some concrete evidence for assessing certain aspects of the children's capabilities.

Children

Familiarisation with the classroom organisation
The children could be involved in a few short, practical, skill-based activities to help familiarise them with the organisation of the room. Often children have their own ideas as to the best way to organise equipment and it may prove helpful to involve them in an evaluation of the systems operating in the room. A personal involvement in the organisation can help encourage the children to adhere to it.

Groupings
As the ability to work in groups is an essential part of design and technology capability, the ways in which the children are grouped for activities will need careful consideration. The membership of the groupings could be based on:

- friendship;
- gender (same and mixed);
- interest;
- practical ability (similar and mixed);
- 'academic' ability (similar and mixed);
- personality (similar and mixed).

There is little research evidence concerning the effectiveness of different groupings at primary level for design and technology and it is certainly an area that needs to be given considerable thought. Some of the main considerations include:

- the participation of all the children in the group;
- the willingness to work with, and alongside, others;
- the sharing out of jobs;
- the constant opting out of jobs which the children dislike/feel diffident about;
- the valuing of others' ideas.

Ways of working
The children can be encouraged to:

- make their own decisions;
- work safely;
- not be wasteful with materials;
- persevere and not rely on others.

Equal opportunities

Special educational needs
Since the Warnock Report found that at any one time up to 20 per cent of the school population could be classified as having 'special educational needs', it is obviously important that this issue is addressed when considering the implementation of the National Curriculum.

Who are these children with special needs? There has been considerable discussion and debate concerning the identification of children with special needs. Those who could be included have needs that are long or short term and which originate from emotional and behavioural difficulties, physical or mental disabilities, or reading and language difficulties. Moreover, it is often overlooked that children who are regarded as 'gifted' should also be included in the category of those with special educational needs.

At the time of the introduction of technology as a foundation subject, three obvious areas had already been identified that might need particular consideration in relation to children with special needs. These were:

Communication
Children can communicate by any means possible, including Makatron, signing, braille, eye communication or the use of a computer.

'Making'
Children with limited manual skills can give instructions to an adult

or peer group member to enable him/her to perform the making part of the activity.

Adaptation of equipment
This might involve the use of larger switches, taps and handles on general equipment, a jig to steady materials when cutting, buzzers and bells instead of a light bulb to check a circuit, and construction kits (rather than other resistant materials) for making models.

There are also certain specific approaches to/features of design and technology that may be used to help overcome some less obvious difficulties that face children with special needs. These include:

1. The use of realistic and relevant situations. The five different contexts in which the activities should be set allow teachers to provide all children with situations that are both realistic and relevant to their particular lifestyles. Fantasy situations may not prove appropriate for children, who find abstract situations and the creation of mental imagery difficult.
2. The use of a range of experiences and learning objectives. The programmes of study and the levels of attainment offer a wide range of experiences and objectives for children of almost all abilities. It is certainly possible for 'gifted' children to be challenged, while allowing the 'less able' to achieve success in their own way. It could be argued that, in terms of the statements of attainment, there is little that some children with severe learning difficulties can achieve, for they may be working towards level 1 for a considerable length of time. In such cases, or indeed for any child experiencing difficulties, teachers could create a series of smaller achievable targets.
3. The open-ended nature of design and technology activity. Since a number of solutions will exist to satisfy the identified need, children with different abilities will be able to achieve 'success' in different ways.
4. A variation in the length of the activity. It is quite possible to involve children in:
   • a number of short activities in order to maintain their interest,
   • a few longer activities which are more demanding and could entail, for example, more in-depth research.
5. A variation in possible outcomes. It is important not to have pre-conceived ideas about the outcomes to be developed by individual children as they often produce surprise results in a practical subject such as design and technology.

To encourage maximum participation by all children, there are certain general approaches which always apply.

- Offer positive statements relating to what the child has, rather than has not, said and done.
- Create a climate where ideas and statements are valued by peers and adults alike.
- Give praise for trying out ideas, even if they are not successful.
- Encourage all children to be included in group work, while still enabling each child to achieve his or her full potential. (Initially, a child could work as an individual within a group.)
- Encourage children to make their own decisions. (A choice between two sizes or colours would be a simple start.)

Gender issues

Although the introduction of the National Curriculum has ensured a minimum entitlement for all, in theory at least, for this to work in practice much will obviously depend on the way that the policy is implemented. It is well known that in certain areas of the curriculum, such as design and technology, boys tend to dominate mixed working groups, to take over the use of the 'making' equipment, and to monopolise the teacher's time.

Boys often feel more confident than girls because of their previous experiences such as watching and helping fathers or older brothers mend various household appliances or tinker with cars and bikes. By contrast, girls may have spent time shopping, helping with household chores and 'caring for others'. It is obviously important to try to counterbalance the social, parental and peer group influences that tend to undermine the achievement of equal opportunities for both sexes.

In the specific area of 'making' in design and technology, what strategies can be tried to encourage equal opportunities for girls?

- Are the groups in which they work varied?
- Are they:
  - all-girl groups?
  - all-girl pairs?
  - boy/girl pairs?
  - small equally mixed groups of boys and girls?
- Are girls' ideas, models and skills praised in front of the boys?
- Do an equal numbers of girls and boys have their models labelled and on display (assuming of course that there is a roughly equal boy/girl ratio in the class)?
- Are girls allowed first choice of equipment, materials and construction kits?
- Are contexts 'girl-friendly'? (Topics such as 'Machines' or 'Transport' may not appeal to them.)
- Are the construction kits stored in areas of the room which are used more by girls, such as the book corner and the home corner?
- Are the children offered female 'role' models?

Conversely, are similar strategies used to encourage equal participation by the boys in activities which are concerned primarily with food, textiles and art and design?

Multicultural perspectives

It is important that the multi-ethnic society in which we live is reflected in the teaching of design and technology as in all other areas of the curriculum. It is now generally accepted that this is best done not by the creation of a separate study of multicultural issues but by their permeation throughout the whole of the curriculum. Schools that have few or no ethnic minority children should do their best to ensure that their pupils gain an understanding of the cultural diversity that exists in other areas of the country.

It is hoped that the following questions will provide schools with a basis for discussion when considering their own policy. This policy should not be one of passive rhetoric but of active encouragement of all children to study and value cultures other than their own. Indeed, it is laid down in the programmes of study that children should consider the needs and values of individuals and of groups from a variety of backgrounds and cultures.

Equal access to the curriculum
If there are children in the school whose first language is not English, are they disadvantaged because:

- poor expectations of their abilities encourage them to underachieve?
- language difficulties do not allow them to participate fully in activities (for example are they excluded by the use of specific technological vocabulary, complicated instructions or workcards, or an over-emphasis upon written recording)?

Schemes of work
Do the schemes of work:

- help children to recognise that no one culture has the monopoly of technological achievements and inventions?
- use contexts that are within the children's own experiences?
- imply that 'appropriate' technology is 'inferior' technology?
- imply that western values and standards alone should be emulated?

Does the printed literature which is used give illustrations and examples from a variety of cultures? Does this material feature ethnic minorities in a positive way?

Do the children have use of materials and equipment from a variety of cultures?

Resources

Lists of useful addresses, organisations, references for practical ideas and suggestions for further reading appear at the end of this book.

Assessment and record-keeping

As experience of planning and organising design and technology activities is extended, so the issues surrounding assessment will become clarified. Certainly some teachers already feel that if their children are engaged in an appropriate design and technology activity, it is possible to stand back and observe them in action. Indeed, if the activity is open-ended and the children have access to a variety of materials and equipment (that are appropriate for the particular stage of the children's development) the pupils will be able to show their capability.

Nonetheless there are some concerns that are already being identified and addressed in many schools, for unless clear objectives are identified before each session it is difficult to determine what, if anything, has been achieved and to identify and monitor detailed cross-curricular links. For example, it is of far greater value to be aware of 'opportunities for giving and receiving precise instructions as a group member' (English AT1 level 3) than it is simply to identify the fact that the children may be speaking and listening. Although there may be time to talk to individual children, a considerable amount of time is needed in order to discuss effectively different stages of the holistic process with a class of perhaps thirty children.

Activities organisation sheet

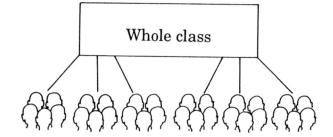

groups – similar activity
e.g. brainstorming, making

report back at end
of session

groups – different design
& technology activity

report back at end
of session

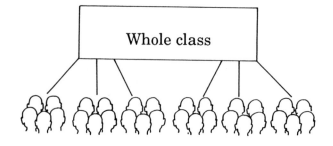

| Groups Design & technology activity | Groups involved in related/ unrelated work | Group Design & technology activity | Groups involved in related/ unrelated work |

10
Curriculum review

Having worked this far through the book, this is an appropriate point to review, and reflect on, existing planning and implementation strategies. While individual teachers, or even year-groups, may have been working together closely, a number of constraints may have prevented the permeation of ideas and practice in depth throughout the school. There are various strategies that might be adopted in order to provide a focus for the review. A staff meeting or a training day would allow staff to share ideas. A series of displays or one main exhibition would help raise the awareness not only of staff and children but also of parents, governors and teachers from feeder schools. (The planning and organisation of such an event could be a design and technology project in itself!)

What should be covered in the review?

Schools may decide to review particular issues that have been raised in the planning and implementation of design and technology, but it would be possible to review in turn each of the four areas that have been identified during the previous stages.

Content

1. A review of both the original planning strategy and the associated schemes of work may help to determine future policy. If staff have started with a topic, a comparison with the programmes of study could be made to identify any areas that have not been covered. (Mechanisms, energy sources and economic considerations have already been identified as areas that are often not covered by more general activities.) If staff have started with the programmes of study, issues such as the possibly contrived nature of the tasks undertaken will need to be discussed. Such reviews may or may not lead to changes in the way in which overall planning takes place.
2. A review of the use of different opportunities (everyday occurrences, special projects or general topic work) may help to determine their future role.

3. A review of the materials and techniques that the children have used may help to identify the need both for particular resources and for progression in their use.

Organisation and management

- A review of the co-ordinator's role:
- A review of classroom organisation;
- A review of equal opportunities.

Matters to be discussed could include:

- to what extent have children with special needs been integrated? What particular achievements and shortcomings can be identified?
- to what extent have girls and boys been given equal opportunities? What strategies have been used? What, if any, changes in attitudes and actions have been noted?
- to what extent have children been involved in work which values, and enables them to extend, their knowledge of other cultures?

Resources
- A review of their storage and replenishment;
- A review of their suitability and possible needs for more/different resources;
- A review of progression in their use and the possible need to develop a planning sheet to identify this progression (similar to the software planning sheet).

Assessment and record-keeping

- A review of the planning sheets that have been used for design and technology activity;
- A review of methods of collecting evidence of individual children's capability;
- A review of methods of recording this information.

Conclusion

As with any curriculum area, constant review and renewal is desirable and this will involve schools in the cyclical process which has been developed throughout this book. Some ideas and practices already exist; others are innovations, and changes will inevitably be necessary. However, if one fundamental change is to be brought about by the introduction of design and technology capability into the primary curriculum, for the writer at least, it would be the emphasis on the involvement of the children in the identification of needs and opportunities, encouraging and enabling them to develop the ability to think for themselves and to think creatively.

References

Design and Technology for Ages 5 to 16: Proposals from the Secretary of State for Education and Science and the Secretary of State for Wales, DES/WO, June 1989

Education for Economic and Industrial Understanding (Curriculum Guidance series No. 4), NCC, April 1990

English in the National Curriculum, DES/WO, March 1990

A Guide to Teacher Assessment: Packs A, B & C and *Assessment Folder*, SEAC, December 1989

Health Education (Curriculum Guidance series No. 5), NCC, July 1990

Mathematics in the National Curriculum, DES/WO, March 1989

National Curriculum Art Working Group: Interim Report, DES/WO, 1991

National Curriculum Design and Technology Working Group: Interim Report, DES/WO, 1988

National Curriculum Consultation Report: Technology, NCC, November 1989

National Curriculum Task Group on Assessment and Testing: A Report, DES/WO, January 1988

Non-Statutory Guidance: Design and Technology Capability, NCC, April 1990

Non-Statutory Guidance: Information Technology Capability, NCC, April 1990

Science in the National Curriculum, DES/WO, March 1989

Technology in the National Curriculum, DES/WO, March 1990

The Whole Curriculum, (Curriculum Guidance series No. 3) NCC, March 1990

Resources

Useful addresses

A & L Scientific and Optical Equipment
190 West Drive, Cleveleys, Blackpool, Lancashire FY 5 2EJ
(*useful equipment*)

Central Supplies Organisation
Sheffield City Council, Staniforth Road, Sheffield S9 3GZ
(*useful equipment*)

Lego UK Ltd.
Wrexham, Clywd LL13 7TQ

Philip Harris Ltd.
Lynn Lane, Shenstone, Staffordshire WS14 0EE

Spectrum Educational Supplies
Unit 2, Maskell Estate, Stephenson Street, London E16 4SA

Technology Teaching Systems Ltd.
Penmore House, Hasland, Chesterfield, Derbyshire S41 0SJ
(*equipment includes tool boards for food and textiles*)

Organisations

A.S.E.
College Lane, Hatfield, Hertfordshire AL10 GAA

B.I.S.
10 Lombard Street, London EC3V 9AT

Centre for Alternative Technology
Machynlleth, Powys SY20 9AZ

Conservation Trust
National Environmental Education Centre, George Palmer Site,
Northumberland Avenue, Reading, Berkshire RG2 7PW

D.A.T.A.
Smallpiece House, 27 Newbold Terrace East, Leamington Spa,
Warwickshire CV32 4ES

Department of Energy
1 Palace Street, Victoria, London SW1E 5HE

The Design Council
28 Haymarket, London SW1Y 45U

Keep Britain Tidy Group
Premier House, 12–13 Hatton Garden, London EC1 2NL

Nature Conservancy Council
Interpretative Branch, Attingham Park, Shrewsbury, Shropshire
SY4 4TW

NCET
Unit 6, Sir William Lyons Road, Science Park, University of
Warwick, Coventry CV4 7EZ

RoSPA
Education Department, Cannon House, The Priory, Queensway,
Birmingham, B4 6BS

RSPB
The Lodge, Sandy, Bedfordshire. SG19 2DL

'Watch'
22 The Green, Nettleham, Lincoln, LN2 2NR

Useful references for practical ideas

Brainwaves: Designing and Making Towards Technology, Scholars
Town Education, 1989

Brainwaves: Designing and Making Primary Design, Scholars Town
Education, 1989

Gilbert, C., *First Look* and *Look Technology*, Oliver & Boyd, 1989 and
1987

Harrison, P., and Ryan, C., *Technology in Action Key Stage 1* and *Key
Stage 2*, Folens, 1990 and 1991

Johnsey, R., *Design and Technology through School Science*,
Macdonald, 1985

'Know How Books', Usborne, 1977. Titles include *Paper Fun, Puppets, Paint & Print* and *Action Toys and Games*

Prestt, B. (ed.), *Scienceworld Teachers' Books A B C* and *1 2 3 4*, Longman, 1986

Primary Technology Resource Pack, City of Newcastle-upon-Tyne, 1989

Williams, P. and Jinks, D., *Design and Technology (5–13)* , Falmer, 1985

This list is indicative; there is a constant flow of new books.

Further reading

BOOKS

Bentley, M., Campbell, J., Lewies, A., and Sullivan, M. (eds), *Primary Design and Technology in Practice*, Longman, 1990

Craft, Design and Technology from 5 to 16 (Curriculum Matters series No. 9), HMI, 1985

Home Economics from 5 to 16 (Curriculum Matters series No. 5), HMI, 1985

Information Technology from 5 to 16 (Curriculum Matters series No. 15), HMI, 1989

Lever, C., *National Curriculum Design and Technology for Key Stages 1, 2 and 3*, Trentham Books, 1990

Tickle, L. (ed.) *Design and Technology in the Primary School Classroom*, Falmer Press, 1990

JOURNALS

The Big Paper, Design Council, 28 Haymarket, London SW1Y 4SU

Questions, 6/7 Hockley Hill, Birmingham, B18 5AA

Special Children, 6/7 Hockley Hill, Birmingham, B18 5AA (*for special and mainstream schools*)

Child Education, Scholastic Publications, Marlborough House, Hollywalk, Leamington Spa, Warwickshire CV32 4LS

Junior Education, Scholastic Publications, Marlborough House, Hollywalk, Leamington Spa, Warwickshire CV32 4LS

Art and Craft Scholastic Publications, Marlborough House, Hollywalk, Leamington Spa, Warwickshire CV32 4LS

Design and Technology Teaching, Data Journal, Smallpiece House, 27 Newbold Terrace East, Leamington Spa, Warwickshire CV32 4ES